In 2015, I was honored with an anonymous nomination for the John C. Maxwell Leadership Award. I was humbled by the nomination, which began a process of interviews over several months. Once selected as one of the top 30 finalists, the process provided for comments from the public. I've selected a few that were submitted under my name. These comments show what is possible when focusing on the *Nine Behaviors of a Servant Leader,* and served as my reward for making the journey. Start your own journey today and you will be lifted up by those you influence through service.

—Art Barter

Mr. Barter is an incredible inspiration in our community. He is a model servant leader and his support for the students of Vista Unified School District has had a positive impact that will resonate for many years in the future. Our leadership team has been energized by his talks on servant leadership and he has catalyzed a shift that is helping us to actualize our core values of respect, trust, and collaboration. —Devin Vodicka, EdD, Superintendent of Schools, Vista Unified School District

Art's dedication to our community is unparalleled, and his commitment to living a life of service is inspiring. He is a leader in the truest sense of the word, both in business and in philanthropy. I am grateful to lean on him as a trusted advisor and honored to call him friend. No one is more deserving of this recognition than Art. —Kevin Crawford, City Manager, Carlsbad

My congratulations to you Art on this most deserving distinction! You truly epitomize the quote, "Your people don't care how much you know until they know how much you care." You have inspired me to become a better leader through your example and your Servant Leadership Institute. Thank you for your being a role model of leadership and philanthropic spirit. Your incredible generosity to your community is so very much appreciated! —Brad Holland, CEO Boys and Girls Club of Carlsbad

My very positive comments about Art Barter. He treats the employees as human beings, he always tells us "families first," he encourages us to persevere practicing the values and principals as human beings, he tells us to serve each other, he also serves the community as well. Thanks Art for supporting the employees so we are able to support our families. —Jose Ramirez, Datron

There seems to be 48 hours in a day for Art and he uses most of them to serve others. No matter what he is doing, what commitments he has, or how low on fuel he is, Art swells up energy to be available, to be engaged, and to be a blessing to those in need. Truly the characteristics of a leader I want to emulate. Thanks Art for all you do in your 48-hour day. Congratulations on being recognized for your service to many. —Roland Shaw, President

Art has a goal: to model and teach leaders to lead with Servant Leadership, and he does it well. A corollary goal is to teach Servant Leadership by being a Servant, not a "Master" he does it with excellence. In his own journey he is quick to take responsibility and very slow to blame others; he is a master at asking "What part of this issue is mine?" And when he sees inconsistency he asks "Do you really believe what you believe?" I am fortunate to be in a CEO/

Leader group with Art and he is both a contributor and a learner. His constant journey to serve others is an inspiration to all. —Werner Jacobsen, Convene Chair

Art is so committed to leadership that he created the Servant Leadership Institute. I have watched as he shares his passion—igniting the fire, one leader at a time, changing the world and touching the lives of leaders who will in turn inspire countless others over a lifetime. I am one. There are many. —Kathy West, Executive Director, Epilepsy Foundation of San Diego County

Art is a true example of an exemplary servant leader who is always humbled by any attention for his magnificent deeds. All who know him are impacted positively and have a sense of calm based on his demeanor and common sense approach to local and global issues. He has always led by example with: his faith; the love and care he provided to his parents; devotion to his wonderful wife Lori and children; his love of mankind; his business sense with loyalty to his employees; and overall philanthropy. Art has made such an impact to non-profit organizations and thousands of lives in San Diego County and other parts of the world. I feel blessed to know Art Barter and think he is a totally befitting candidate for the John Maxwell Leadership Award. You too would be proud to know Art, share his sincerity and see his passion for God and serving others. —Rita Geldert, Retired City Manager, Vista

As a member of several non-profit boards, I can honestly say that I know of no one single person who has had a greater impact on our North County San Diego community than Art Barter. Art's generosity and his willingness to make a difference not only humbles me, it STAGGERS me! Art's living example of Servant Leadership soundly demonstrates that "Bottom Up" Leadership is not just the best model out there, but the ONLY one! Let me join all of San Diego in congratulating you, Art on this well-deserved recognition! —Michael Donaldson, Kiwanis Club of Escondido, Escondido Education Foundation

Quiet, smart, quick, generous, giving, caring, committed, inspirational, relentless, husband, father, friend, community leader, are all descriptors that come immediately to my mind about Art Barter. But none of them on their own, or in combination, adequately communicate either what an awesome human being he is, or the enormous positive impact he has had on our community, or on the thousands of people worldwide who have been and continue to be positively influenced by his Servant Leadership organization and work. Congrats and thanks for all you do Art. —Jim Minarik, Chairman, DEI Holdings, Inc

Art Barter is an icon in the North San Diego County community and has inspired me to be able to overcome very difficult times that I have faced in my life personally. I consider him to be a mentor and friend but I am sure that there are many people who believe that Art is their mentor. Art is an example of how someone should live their life. While Art has had challenges in his own life, and overcome them, unlike many people in that situation the scars of the challenges he has faced and overcome are invisible. He is an extraordinary leader and role model. —Larry B. Anderson, CEO

I met Art over a decade ago when I was invited to speak at a Datron World Communications meeting. Very early on I realized that he was a special leader. It

was the first time I saw the practice of listening to employees, considering their views, inviting criticisms of his own views, clearly demonstrated as a leadership strength and not a weakness. His commitment to the practice of leading from the bottom up and from inside out has only deepened and I believe this is the way of the future in terms of getting the very best out of each and every human being in any organization. He is for me, already a winner. —Chris Stokes, Jamaican Bobsled Olympic Team

Art has been an inspiration to us at WD-40 Company for many years. His concepts of Servant Leadership are embedded in our leadership development efforts globally. He has given selflessly of his time to the employees participating in our Leadership Laboratory series of courses. His Servant Leadership Institute continues to give back to the business community without a single thought of recompense. Art is the embodiment of living one's values while growing a phenomenally successful business. Values and performance are not in contest with each other. Art proves that values in leadership are the prerequisites for business success. Thank you, Art, for all that you do, and all that you are. —Stan Sewitch, VP Global Org Development, WD-40 Company

Through Art's leadership over the last 18 years, I have learned to be a servant leader myself. I have been challenged, praised, sometimes corrected, but always treated as a person of value. Because of Art and Lori's heart to serve the worldwide community through the manufacture of quality communications equipment, the Datron Charitable Fund and the Servant Leadership Institute, I have the joy of knowing the fruit of my work has touched lives around the world. Priceless! —Carol Malinski, SLI and Datron

Wow what a journey... approximately 18 years ago I met Art Barter and joined the Datron Organization, 8 years into this role I began the transition with Art Barter and the entire Datron Management team on our journey into Servant Leadership. It's amazing what an impact Art and his values have done to transform Datron and ALL of the People we Impact. The concept of Leading from the HEART is the inspiration I have discovered under Art's leadership. He is an amazing Leader and as a result we are constantly impacting the People we influence based on our Servant Leadership Culture!!! —Roger Gillespie, Datron

Art's approach to leadership is candid, transparent and humbling. He uses his own life expamples of how mistakes can become cornerstones of success. He challenges participants to self-reflect and commit to change. Art teaches core values and strategies any leader can follow if they are willing to make the single most important investment, an investment in others. —Denise Hujing, BB&T

Art Barter is an exemplary leader. He influences through service and his humble, caring, selfless concern for his people and the community have inspired and equipped countless leaders here in San Diego and beyond. Art has taught that leadership isn't just about getting results but it is also in the "how" you get those results. He is indeed transforming the soul of leadership as he builds trust, inspires greatness, and helps others lead from their hearts to discover no limits to their potential. Art has shown the business and non-profit worlds that trust is not merely a social virtue but also an economic driver. His leadership is truly about building up and equipping others to find the best version of themselves.
—Mark Kalpakgian, Classical Academies

THE SERVANT LEADERSHIP JOURNAL

An
18 Week
Journey
To Transform
You and Your
Organization

Art Barter

ISBN: 978-0-9986711-0-9

Servant Leadership Institute
1959 Palomar Oaks Way, Suite 200
Carlsbad, CA 92011

CONTENTS

ACKNOWLEDGEMENTS

I would like to thank the team at the Servant Leadership Institute for their work in helping complete this project. They are a great team of servant leaders who desire to inspire and equip you through your own servant leadership journey. I especially want to thank the following people:

Lisa Courtemanche, my Executive Assistant, who has run my life for the past two years. Thank you for your servant's heart and your desire to help me be the best I can be.

Nonie Jobe, my writer and editor, our second project together. Thank you for your servant's heart using your talents to add value to others.

The leadership team at Datron, which participated, witnessed and survived my transformation. You have been a big part in developing my servant leadership behaviors. Thank you for acknowledging no one is perfect and for the grace you extend to me when my old "power" leader behaviors come out. Your honest feedback has blessed me in so many ways.

The team at Weaving Influence who helped us move this project over the finish line with their great team of professionals.

Ken Blanchard, who challenged my leadership beliefs in 2003. Your writings on servant leadership and your mentoring have transformed my life; for that I am eternally grateful.

My family—Lori, my wife and best friend, and Jennifer and Chris, who were on the front lines of my transformation. Thank you for your unconditional love during those tough years before I realized I needed to change. I love you.

INTRODUCTION

Welcome to the *Servant Leadership Journal.* The purpose of this journal is to help you change your leadership behaviors. I personally like to look at leadership from a servant's perspective, with a focus on servant leadership—but don't let the word "servant" keep you from making the most important change you'll ever make in your leadership beliefs.

I was a product of the corporate power model. After graduating from college in 1979, I entered into training in the command-and-control corporate world. I embraced the command-and-control leadership model and, in fact, made it the most important priority in my life. At the young age of 24, I was put into my first management role, and at 25, I was pushed into the senior finance role in my division with the title of "Controller." I had a real desire to succeed in life; because I was driving a company car, had a senior leadership role in a company, and was empowered to direct the actions of others, I thought I had arrived. I embraced my new title with all my heart, but the only trouble was, my heart was nowhere to be found in most of my decisions as a leader. Don't get me wrong; at the time I believed I was a great leader. From that point forward, I literally sacrificed everything in my life for success.

When I was challenged in my leadership beliefs by Ken Blanchard in 2003, I was ready for a change. I had just been "burned," again, by my employer and was tired of giving my all to a corporate world that didn't care about me or my family. Sound familiar? At the time of this writing, the engagement level of the workforce in the U.S. is at an all-time low of 30 percent. In addition, Gallup does an annual poll that surveys the confidence we have in our country's institutions. Congress is last on the list (no surprise here) with the lowest confidence level—less than 10 percent—and the confidence level for corporations runs at about 25 percent. I recently heard a senior leader in the survey industry say we are a country of very lonely individuals.

As Ken Blanchard, John Maxwell, and most of the other experts in the field teach, leadership is all about influence. I started looking at and changing my leadership beliefs in 2004. Change is a funny thing. It sounds great and looks good, but it feels like...well, you fill in the blank. In my case, I had to face the reality that changing my behaviors was the only way I could convince those I influenced that I was serious about changing the way I lead others, that I really cared.

"Walk the talk" was a very popular catch phrase during that time, but most of the leaders who were saying it didn't really believe in it. Or maybe they believed in it, but they didn't understand it. They thought if they got out of their office and walked around on a regular basis, that meant they were "walking their talk." I worked in a company where the CEO literally scheduled a time once every week to walk around the company. The employees loved it; they knew that at the same time each week he would come around and say hi to them. Mind you, he didn't pay them very well, they were never allowed to participate in the company's bonus program and their medical benefits were no better than standard. The company had no mission or purpose, nor was there a culture with any type of collective collaboration. In that company, I reported to a division president. Over the first five years of my tenure with that company, I worked for four different division presidents.

I believe leaders need to back up their talk with behaviors. I found a conceptual paper recently that proposes a very telling definition of destructive leadership behavior, along with a descriptive model. The authors defined destructive leadership behavior as: "The systematic and repeated behavior by a leader, supervisor, or manager that violates the legitimate interest of the organization

[sic] by undermining and/or sabotaging the organization's [sic] goals, tasks, resources, and effectiveness and/or the motivation, well-being or job satisfaction of his/her subordinates."[1]

As you think about this definition, keep in mind that we have the lowest engagement of U.S. workers in our nation's history. The good news is, this can change if we as leaders are willing to change. I believe we can.

I started the Servant Leadership Institute in 2010, after I had spent six years implementing servant leadership in the radio company I had purchased in 2004. As we were starting our journey of change at Datron, we searched for training material or programs that were available in the marketplace to help us implement servant leadership in our company. In the end, we decided to create our own training program for our employees. We developed three training modules of 15 hours each, totaling 45 hours of training for every employee in our radio company. Through the experiences we gained during that process, along with feedback from our employees, we developed the Nine Behaviors of a Servant Leader. We believe these behaviors are key to becoming a better leader—one who focuses on others first and would like to see all "destructive leadership behavior" eliminated.

One of the tools I used to change my own behavior was journaling. Every couple days, I would spend time writing about my experiences, feelings, challenges and goals which led to a better understanding of where I wanted to go. Sometimes I would write down ideas, sometimes goals and sometimes just thoughts. That

---

[1]Ståle Einarsen, Merethe Schanke Aasland, Anders Skogstad, "Destructive leadership behavior: A definition and conceptual model," *The Leadership Quarterly,* Vol. 18 (2007), pg. 207–216.

time of journaling and reflection provided the basis for the change I wanted to make in my leadership behaviors.

Today, I want to pass this tool on to you. This journal will allow you to walk through the nine behaviors I feel are so key to becoming a servant leader. Let's change that old, worn out saying, "Walk the Talk" to "Behave your Talk.™" Show others you are serious about becoming a different type of leader—one who can be trusted to act the same as your talk, one who really cares.

We are on this journey together. Dedicate time to walk through these behaviors. I believe there are four distinct steps for you to take in your journey with each behavior:

Educate yourself on the meaning of each behavior. Use Google, Wikipedia or whatever you need to gain an understanding of what the behavior means.

Understand where you are on each behavior. Be realistic in your review; ask others, including your spouse, to tell you how you behave. Be courageous to see the real you.

Apply what you are learning to your life. What specific areas do you want to improve in? What specific traits related to each behavior do you what to change? Set daily goals to affect that change.

Reflect. Record the results of your journey—what you've learned about yourself, what others have noticed, how you feel about the change you are making, and what else you would like to do to continue your journey in each behavior.

Once you have completed this cycle, start it all over again for as long as it takes to change each behavior.

A word of caution: Your old behaviors are hard to eliminate. The longer you've been trained in the command-and-control power world, the longer it will take to change those behaviors. And another word of caution: Know that when you are under pressure and the stress level in your life increases, those old behaviors will show themselves. That's okay. Recognize it, apologize for it, journal about it, and get better. It is not the end of the world. Trust me; I know this part of the transformation better than I would like to admit.

You've already started the journey; now start writing. When I first started journaling, it was not comfortable for me, nor was it easy. Changing our behaviors is not easy, but it is possible. Join me on this journey and make our world a better place.

I'm on this journey with you every step of the way!

Chapter 1

INTENTIONAL SERVANT LEADERSHIP

I began my intentional journey into servant leadership in 2004. This journal will lead you through the same steps I took to help me be intentional in changing my leadership behaviors away from the traditional self-serving power mode to one based on servanthood. I believe the word "servant" is the most important word in servant leadership, but maybe not for the reasons you might suspect. "Authentic," "values-based," "situational," etc. are all labels put on leadership beliefs, but none are related to action; they are all simply adjectives, while "servant" implies action. Action is what is needed in leadership today—action that puts others first, not ourselves.

In our journey toward implementing intentional servant leadership in our companies, we stumbled out of the gate; it took us about two years to get a handle on what would work for us. And that is an important point: You need to find what works for you. You know yourself better than anyone else, weaknesses and all. For me, the discipline required to intentionally change my leadership beliefs required a model I could commit to. I believe my approach to becoming intentional in learning the servant leader behaviors is easy to follow, and journaling will give you a great foundation to build on as you change your leadership behavior.

I found writing in a journal rather than typing on the computer helped me to be more intentional about the process. It kept me from checking email, reading the alerts that popped up on my screen, or answering alerts from social media. Another plus is that it gives you something tangible to go back and read later in your journey. You'll be so amazed at the progress you have made over time that you may even want to make notes in the margin about how far you've come.

I would encourage you to work on one behavior each month. I found this helped me solidify the learning experience, but more importantly, it gave me time to change my daily behavior as a leader. I've provided two weeks of space in your journal to write. There will be days you will not journal; you will spend time learning and reflecting. Set a goal to write every other day if you prefer. If you find you would like to spend more than two weeks on a behavior, we have provided space at the back of your journal for those extra writing days.

The four steps of intentional servant leadership are simple and it's best if you follow the process on a regular basis. I recommend a daily routine—one of learning, understanding, application and then reflection. Each day you will start with what you learned from the goals and results you observed from the previous day. You will then learn from those experiences and additional study on the behavior, understand how that might apply to your life and your leadership, and apply what you have learned by setting one or two goals. At the end of the day, or the first thing the next morning, journal the results and what you learned. Then start the process all over again, taking what you learned the previous day and adding it to what you learn new that day. Always take time to learn something new about the behavior you are working on.

1. Learn about the behavior you are working on. Search the Internet, go back through leadership books you've read, look up quotes on the subject and ask others for their definition. Find a constant source of learning. The Appendix in the back of this journal has a list of servant leadership books we recommend to help you in learning how to be intentional about your behaviors.

2. Understand the behavior you are working on. Reflect on your current behaviors and what others are telling you or have told you in the past; ask your spouse, your children, and those you serve to tell you where you stand on that behavior. Once others around you start to understand you are serious about being intentional in your leadership behaviors, input will abound.

3. Apply what you have learned by setting one or two goals for that day. Make them intentional goals that can be accomplished in 24 hours. Don't create a long list of goals you know you will not be able to accomplish; don't overcommit. This circle works best if you can accomplish your goals on a regular basis.

4. Reflect. Record your results and anything you may have learned about yourself. Results are a requirement for leaders; without them, we cannot be successful in transforming to our intentional behaviors. There will be days when you may not feel you're making progress, or days when an old behavior may come out. That's okay—don't give up.

Stay consistent with these four steps each day. The journey is worth it. The change you will see in yourself and the reaction of others will be truly priceless. I remember early in the process, my wife Lori told me, "If this works for you, it can work for anyone." She would later tell me I had become a better husband and father. I was a better person for being intentional about changing my life and my behaviors.

I look forward to hearing your story—about the changes you've made and the reactions of those around you.

Chapter 2

Behavior No. 1 — SERVE FIRST

> *"The world is waiting for us to graduate from ourselves."*
> *—Shannon L. Alder*

My wife Lori, who is my best friend, loves to have coffee ready for her when she gets up in the morning. I don't know why and it really isn't required that I understand why; I desire to make her happy unconditionally. The first thing I do after getting up each morning is make her a fresh pot of coffee. She takes care of me and all my needs. More importantly, she makes our house our home. When she travels and I stay home with our two cats, Juno and Wiley, the heart of our home is missing. Lori is the best daily example I have of a servant leader. She takes care of our kids, cats, home, and me in an unbelievable way. She serves her family with all her heart and soul, so making her coffee brings me as much joy as it does her.

Serving first sounds easy; however, when our life unfolds each day and we are faced with challenges, our motives are challenged. Your motives need be pure, which is not always easy for most of us. I believe you can transform both your mindset and motives to serve first; it doesn't have to come naturally. The most important measure of serving others is this: Are those you come in contact with better off after they have come in contact with you? This may be easy to accomplish with those we meet for a single moment in time on the streets, in stores or in our community. But what about those we love—our families, spouse, children—or those we spend most of our waking hours with at work? How do we keep our motives pure in serving others? We need to graduate from ourselves. I love this quote from Booker T. Washington: "Those who are happiest are those who do the most for others." When we serve others with a pure heart, we have joy in our lives.

Author Mollie Marti puts it this way: "The more you become aware of and respond to the needs of others, the richer your own life becomes." We should not only serve others; we also need to develop a sense of awareness of their needs before we serve them. Poet and author Harley King raises the bar even higher, saying, "Service to others in their time of need is a privilege and an honor." Albert Einstein said it best: "The high destiny of the individual is to serve rather than to rule."

It's time to start your journaling process. The four steps of transformation we taught in Chapter 1 are what we recommend you use in the next 30 days.

There is no magic amount of time to spend on each of the four areas. This is your journey, your transformation, and you are in control of the speed at which you journal. We have provided enough pages for 14 days of journaling. I will caution you, based on my experience in my journaling, don't rush it. If you have someone you trust, I suggest you share with them what you are learning about yourself and your journey in the behaviors of servant leaders. Start with the learning process. Take some time to study what it means to serve. Then take what you've learned and make sure you understand how it might apply to your own life. Once you feel you have an idea of what you would like to accomplish, initiate some goals you want to accomplish in your day-to-day life. Then leave room to reflect on the results you experience in your journey.

Spend time every day in your journal. It may feel uncomfortable at first but, stick with it. Those you influence will start to see a difference in how you behave. Record the challenges you face so you can look back at some time in the future to see your progress. Now, pick up a pen and get started. Remember, I'm on this journey with you.

DAY 1

What I've learned today about serving first:

How might what I've learned apply to my life?

What will I do tomorrow to serve someone?

Reflection:

DAY 2

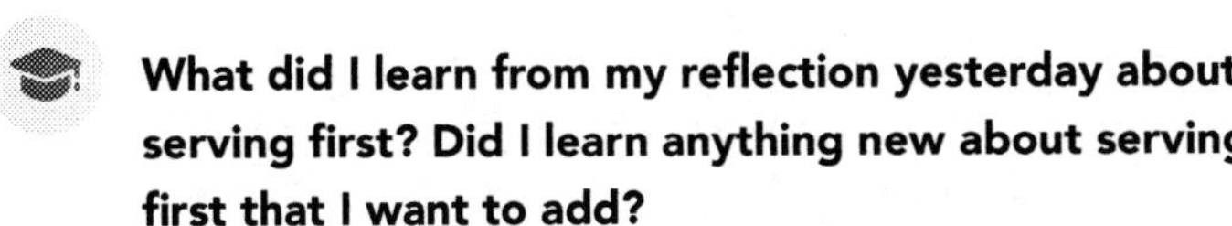

What did I learn from my reflection yesterday about serving first? Did I learn anything new about serving first that I want to add?

How might what I've learned apply to my life?

What will I do tomorrow to serve someone?

Reflection:

DAY 3

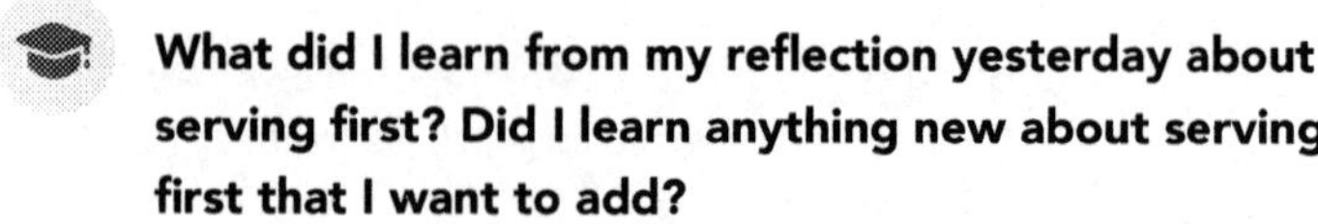

What did I learn from my reflection yesterday about serving first? Did I learn anything new about serving first that I want to add?

How might what I've learned apply to my life?

What will I do tomorrow to serve someone?

Reflection:

DAY 4

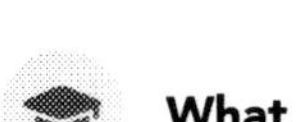

What did I learn from my reflection yesterday about serving first? Did I learn anything new about serving first that I want to add?

How might what I've learned apply to my life?

What will I do tomorrow to serve someone?

Reflection:

"Truly caring is truly liberating."
—Farmer Able in Farmer Able, *by Art Barter*

DAY 5

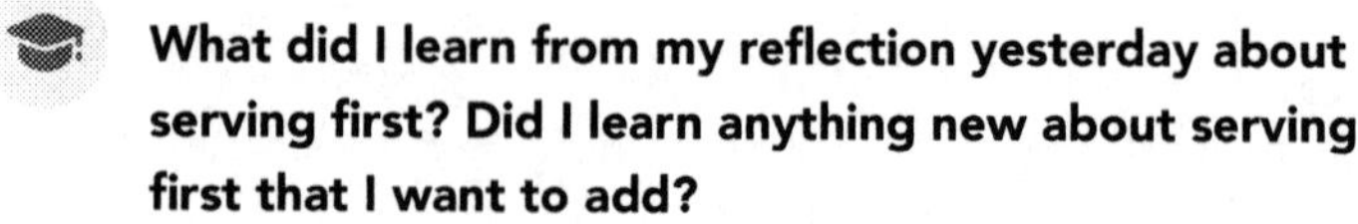

What did I learn from my reflection yesterday about serving first? Did I learn anything new about serving first that I want to add?

How might what I've learned apply to my life?

What will I do tomorrow to serve someone?

Reflection:

DAY 6

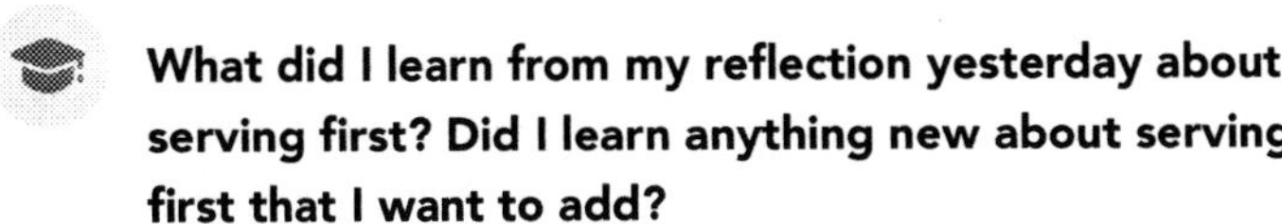

What did I learn from my reflection yesterday about serving first? Did I learn anything new about serving first that I want to add?

How might what I've learned apply to my life?

What will I do tomorrow to serve someone?

Reflection:

DAY 7

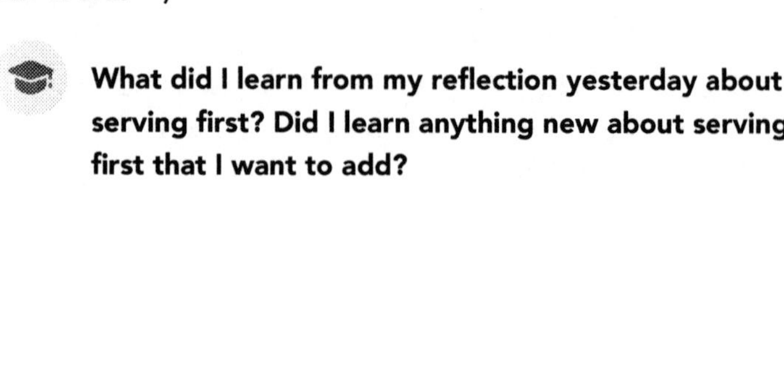

What did I learn from my reflection yesterday about serving first? Did I learn anything new about serving first that I want to add?

How might what I've learned apply to my life?

What will I do tomorrow to serve someone?

Reflection:

"If you're not making someone else's life better, then you're wasting your time. Your life will become better by making other lives better."
—Will Smith

DAY 8

 **What did I learn from my reflection yesterday about serving first? Did I learn anything new about serving first that I want to add?**

How might what I've learned apply to my life?

What will I do tomorrow to serve someone?

Reflection:

DAY 9

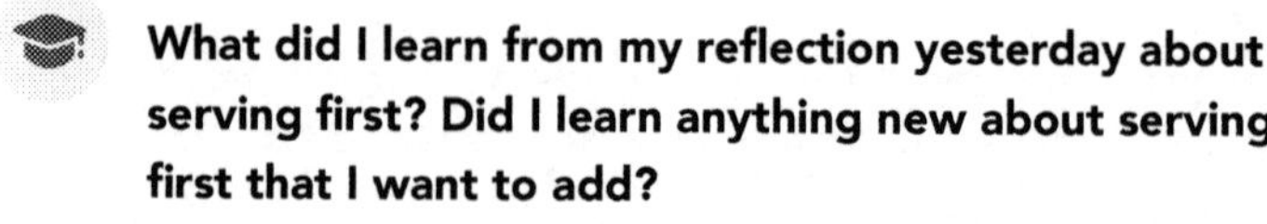

What did I learn from my reflection yesterday about serving first? Did I learn anything new about serving first that I want to add?

How might what I've learned apply to my life?

What will I do tomorrow to serve someone?

Reflection:

DAY 10

What did I learn from my reflection yesterday about serving first? Did I learn anything new about serving first that I want to add?

How might what I've learned apply to my life?

What will I do tomorrow to serve someone?

Reflection:

DAY 11

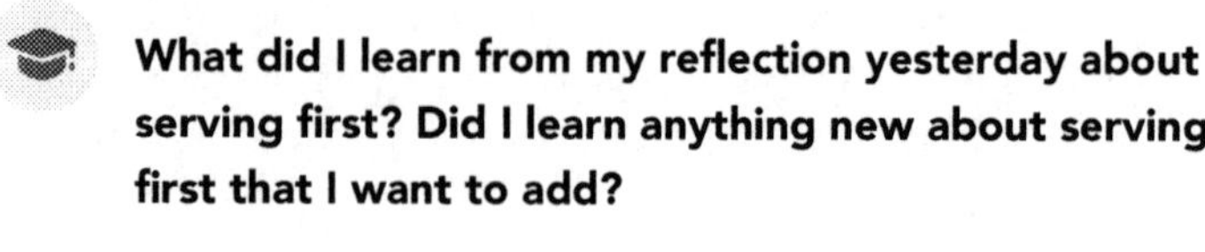

What did I learn from my reflection yesterday about serving first? Did I learn anything new about serving first that I want to add?

How might what I've learned apply to my life?

What will I do tomorrow to serve someone?

Reflection:

DAY 12

What did I learn from my reflection yesterday about serving first? Did I learn anything new about serving first that I want to add?

How might what I've learned apply to my life?

What will I do tomorrow to serve someone?

Reflection:

"Doing nothing for others is the undoing of ourselves."
—Horace Mann

DAY 13

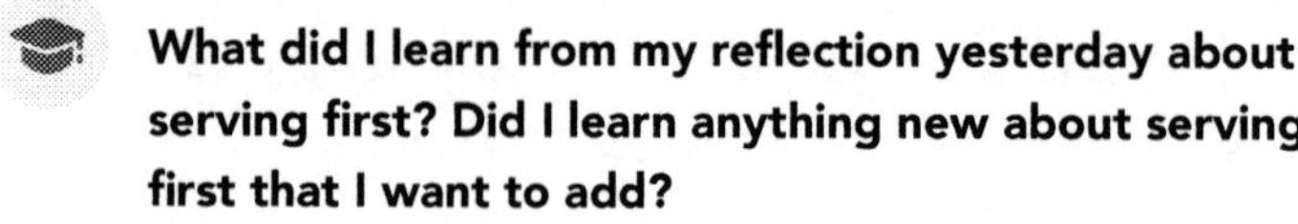

What did I learn from my reflection yesterday about serving first? Did I learn anything new about serving first that I want to add?

How might what I've learned apply to my life?

What will I do tomorrow to serve someone?

Reflection:

DAY 14

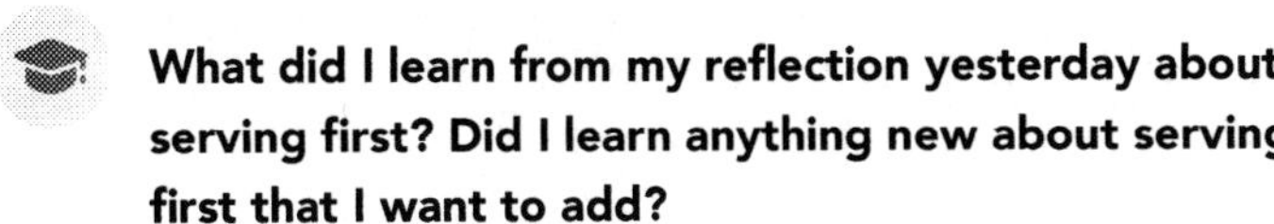

What did I learn from my reflection yesterday about serving first? Did I learn anything new about serving first that I want to add?

How might what I've learned apply to my life?

What will I do tomorrow to serve someone?

Reflection:

You made it! Remember, everyone transforms their behaviors at different rates. Keep that in mind if you are working through this process with others in your organization; this is a transformational journal for you. Don't compare your progress to others.

One of the best tools I was taught while learning to change my behaviors was a visualization exercise. It is a process whereby you identify something you do each day that will remind you of the behavior. Like me, you will feel like a fool the first time you do this. I would encourage you to go through the visualization exercise I've included at the end of each chapter. It is well worth your time and will have a lasting impression on your life.

Your Visualization Exercise—Serving First

The visualization of serving first in my life is making a pot of coffee for my wife Lori as soon as I get up in the morning. Close your eyes and picture what serving first means to you. This will be the picture that will represent serving first to you. Make sure it is a picture of something you do every day. It may include serving a person in your family or in your organization. Make sure it is something you do each and every day.

Write your true life visualization of what serving first means to you.

Congratulations on completing you first behavior of servant leadership. Keep up the great work!

Chapter 3

Behavior No. 2 — BUILD TRUST

> *"The ability to establish, grow, extend, and restore trust is the key professional and personal competency of our time."*
> *—Stephen M.R. Covey*

Building trust is one of the most difficult behaviors required of a leader today. We live in a society that doesn't have a high level of trust, even though we talk about how we value trust, how important it is in our lives or how it is one of our core values.

Like many of you, my route from home to work requires me to drive on the freeway. When we get on the freeway, most of the people sharing the road with us are strangers, and yet amazingly, we extend trust to most of them—trusting them to stay in their lanes, to signal before changing lanes, and to drive safely. The average size of vehicles today ranges from 3,000 to 6,000 pounds, and in California they are driven on average at 70 miles per hour. We trust the strangers driving these vehicles to follow the traffic laws. However, when we arrive at work, we find it difficult to trust those with whom we spend most of our awake time.

In our organization, we take a trust survey every six months. We ask two simple questions of those who follow us: 1) "Do you trust your boss? Yes or no," and 2) "Do you trust management? Yes or no." The result is a metric we call our trust index. The index reflects the percentage of employees that answered yes to each of the questions. After interviewing many people in various companies, Stephen M.R. Covey discovered the question, "Do you trust your boss?" is one of the most accurate indicators of the health of a company.

When trust is broken, you need to invest time convincing the other person you can be trusted again. Invest is the operative word. You cannot talk your way out of a situation your behavior has gotten you into. Convincing the other person you can be trusted again is accomplished through your behaviors. In my servant leadership journey over the past 10 years, I learned I need to trust myself before I can trust others or expect them to trust me. There are counterfeit behaviors in trust. I recommend you read *The Speed of Trust* by Stephen M.R. Covey over the next 30 days. It is one of the best sources and tools to help you build trust as a leader. We have had Stephen with us at several conferences, and he has worked directly with our management team on a number of occasions.

In 2016, all the leaders in our companies, including myself, worked on three trust cards focusing on the behaviors we need to improve. (Read Stephen's book to find out more about trust cards.) One thing that's great about Stephen is he provides examples of what he calls "counterfeit behaviors," those that don't build trust in relationships. For example, there are three ways to communicate trust—or lack of trust—with others: verbal, non-verbal or just being silent. Since most communication is done through non-verbal signs, it's good to have someone you trust help you determine the non-verbal signs that are undermining your work in building trust with others. One of my staff recently helped me understand that I have a "look" (it's a pretty serious frown) when I get frustrated with others. She is helping me understand when that "look" comes out so I can manage it. For others, it might be their tone of voice, and for some, their silence might leave others with the impression of distrust.

As a leader, you need to build trust or others will not follow you. Trusting yourself first and then extending trust to others will give you the right to expect others to trust you. Remember, you can't talk your way out of a situation your behavior got you into. Building trust in others is critical to your long-term influence as a leader.

DAY 1

What I've learned today about building trust:

How might what I've learned apply to my life?

What will I do tomorrow to build trust with someone?

Reflection:

"Contrary to what most people believe, trust is not some soft, illusive quality that you either have or you don't; rather, trust is a pragmatic, tangible, actionable asset that you can create."
—Stephen M.R. Covey

DAY 2

What did I learn from my reflection yesterday about building trust? Did I learn anything new about building trust that I want to add?

How might what I've learned apply to my life?

What will I do tomorrow to build trust with someone?

Reflection:

DAY 3

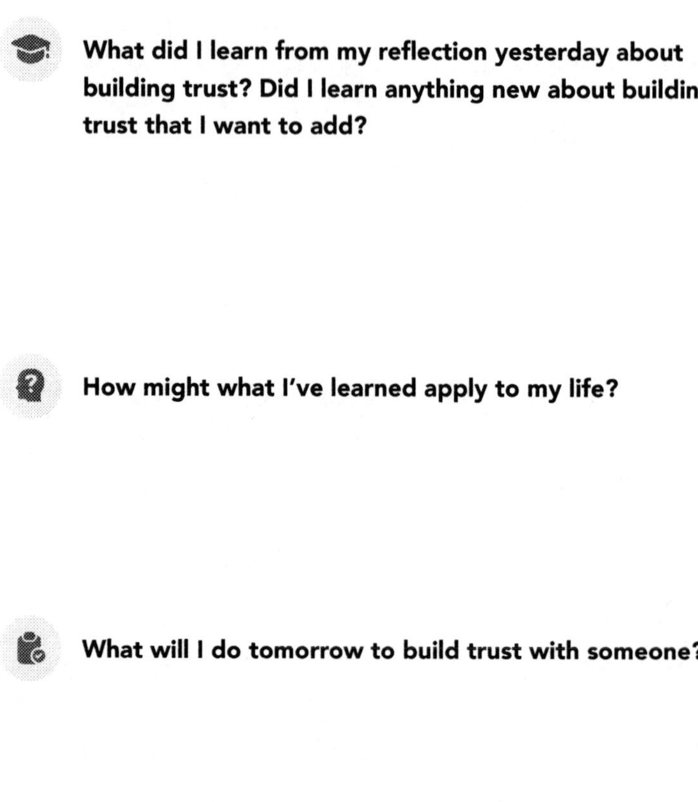

What did I learn from my reflection yesterday about building trust? Did I learn anything new about building trust that I want to add?

How might what I've learned apply to my life?

What will I do tomorrow to build trust with someone?

Reflection:

DAY 4

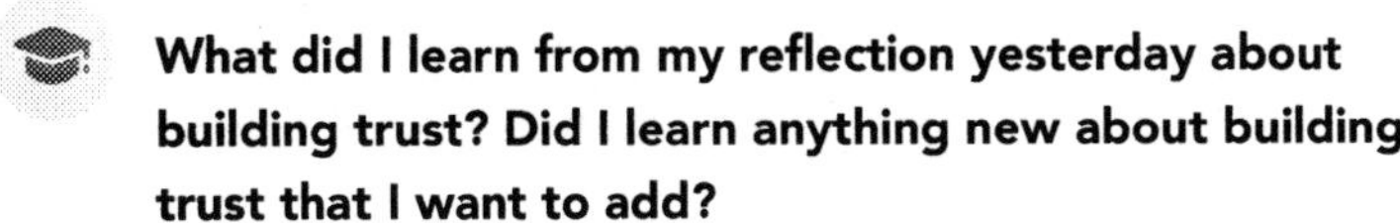

What did I learn from my reflection yesterday about building trust? Did I learn anything new about building trust that I want to add?

How might what I've learned apply to my life?

What will I do tomorrow to build trust with someone?

Reflection:

DAY 5

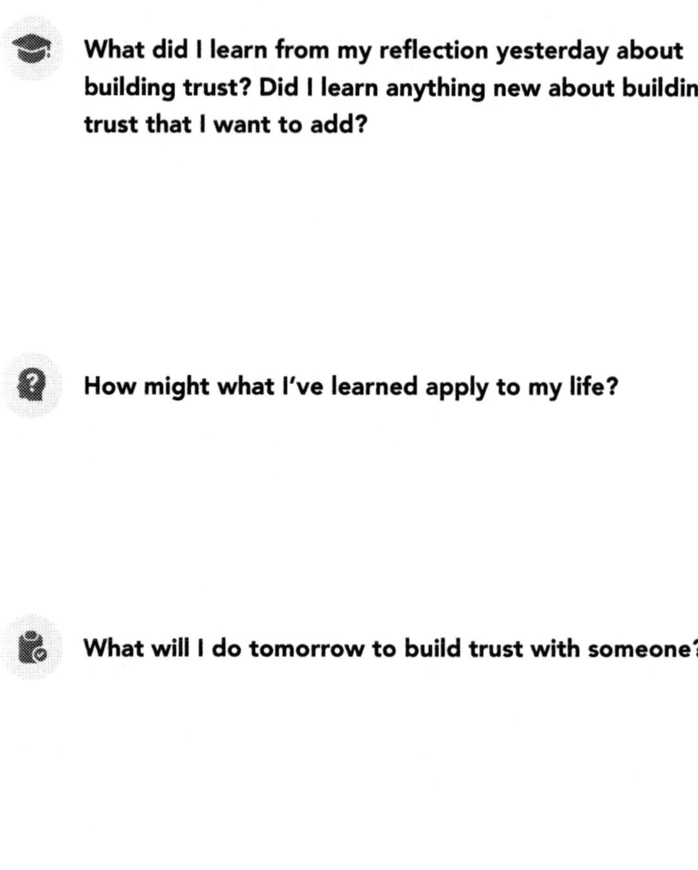

What did I learn from my reflection yesterday about building trust? Did I learn anything new about building trust that I want to add?

How might what I've learned apply to my life?

What will I do tomorrow to build trust with someone?

Reflection:

DAY 6

What did I learn from my reflection yesterday about building trust? Did I learn anything new about building trust that I want to add?

How might what I've learned apply to my life?

What will I do tomorrow to build trust with someone?

Reflection:

DAY 7

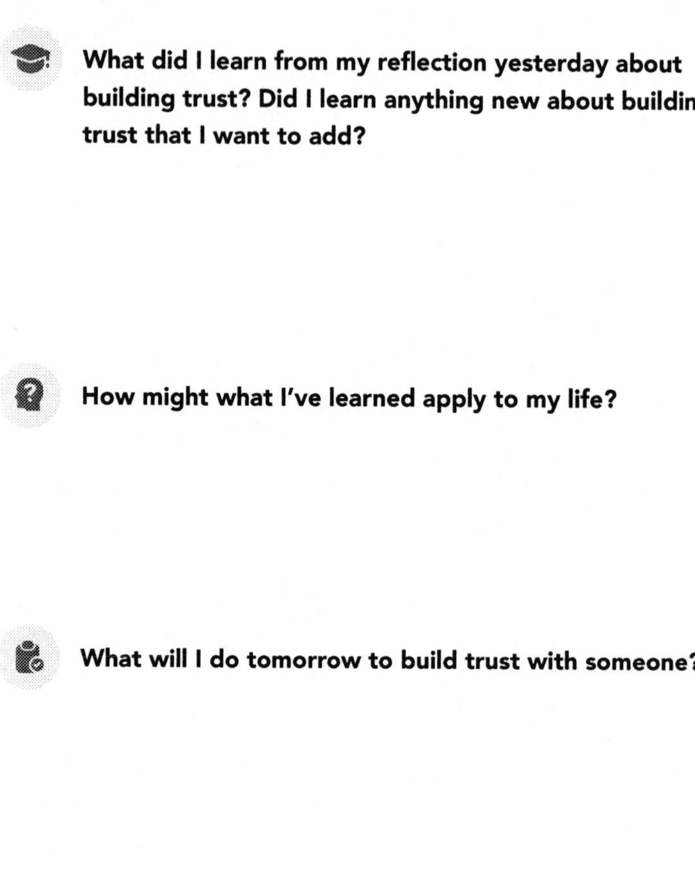

What did I learn from my reflection yesterday about building trust? Did I learn anything new about building trust that I want to add?

How might what I've learned apply to my life?

What will I do tomorrow to build trust with someone?

Reflection:

DAY 8

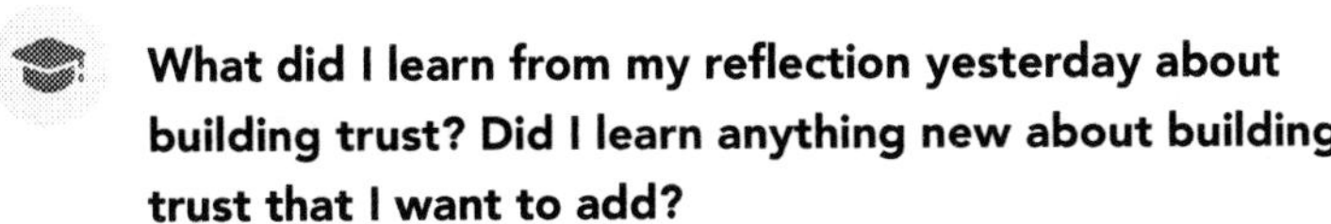

What did I learn from my reflection yesterday about building trust? Did I learn anything new about building trust that I want to add?

How might what I've learned apply to my life?

What will I do tomorrow to build trust with someone?

Reflection:

DAY 9

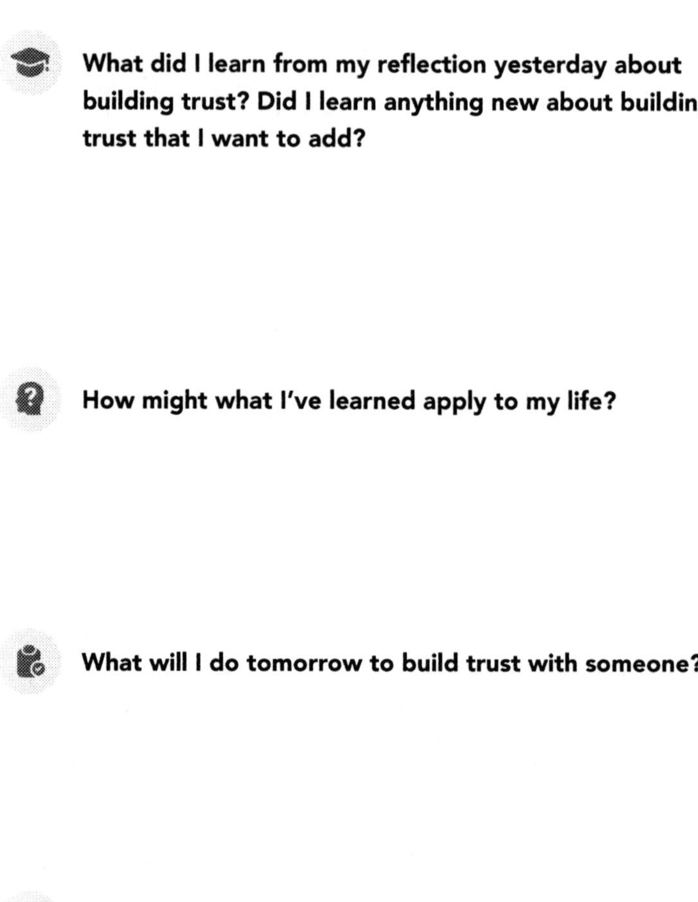

What did I learn from my reflection yesterday about building trust? Did I learn anything new about building trust that I want to add?

How might what I've learned apply to my life?

What will I do tomorrow to build trust with someone?

Reflection:

"Trust is the glue of life. It's the most essential ingredient in effective communication. It's the foundational principle that holds all relationships." —Stephen R. Covey

DAY 10

What did I learn from my reflection yesterday about building trust? Did I learn anything new about building trust that I want to add?

How might what I've learned apply to my life?

What will I do tomorrow to build trust with someone?

Reflection:

DAY 11

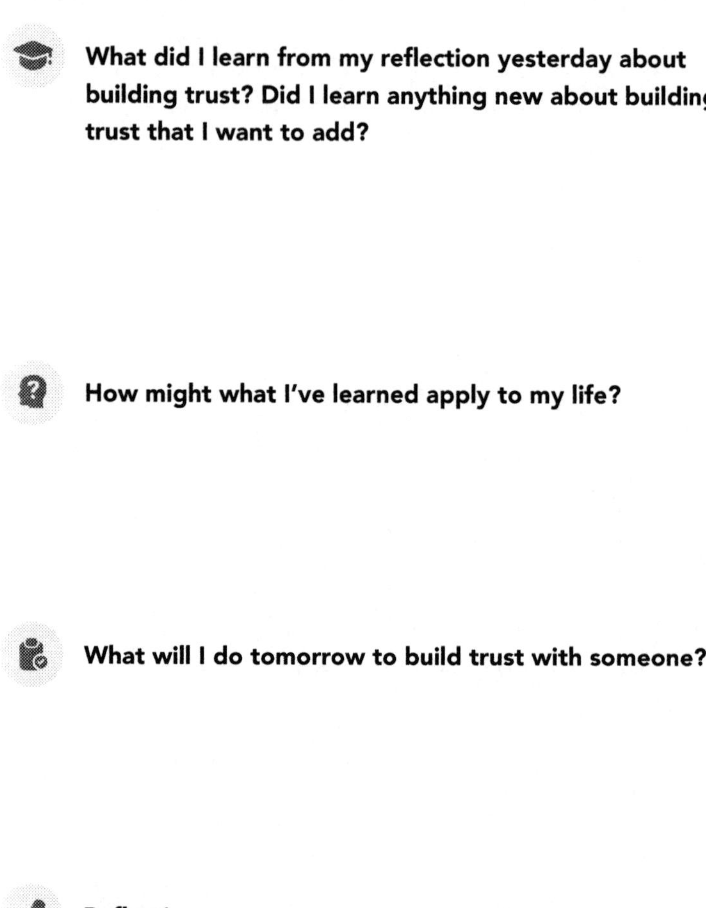

What did I learn from my reflection yesterday about building trust? Did I learn anything new about building trust that I want to add?

How might what I've learned apply to my life?

What will I do tomorrow to build trust with someone?

Reflection:

"Trust is the lubrication that makes it possible for organizations to work." —*Warren Bennis*

DAY 12

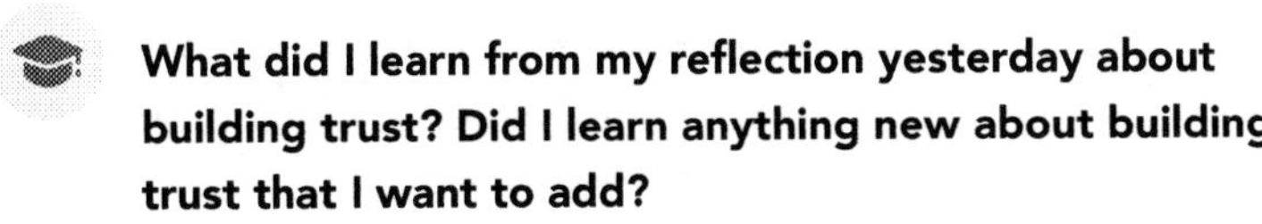

What did I learn from my reflection yesterday about building trust? Did I learn anything new about building trust that I want to add?

How might what I've learned apply to my life?

What will I do tomorrow to build trust with someone?

Reflection:

DAY 13

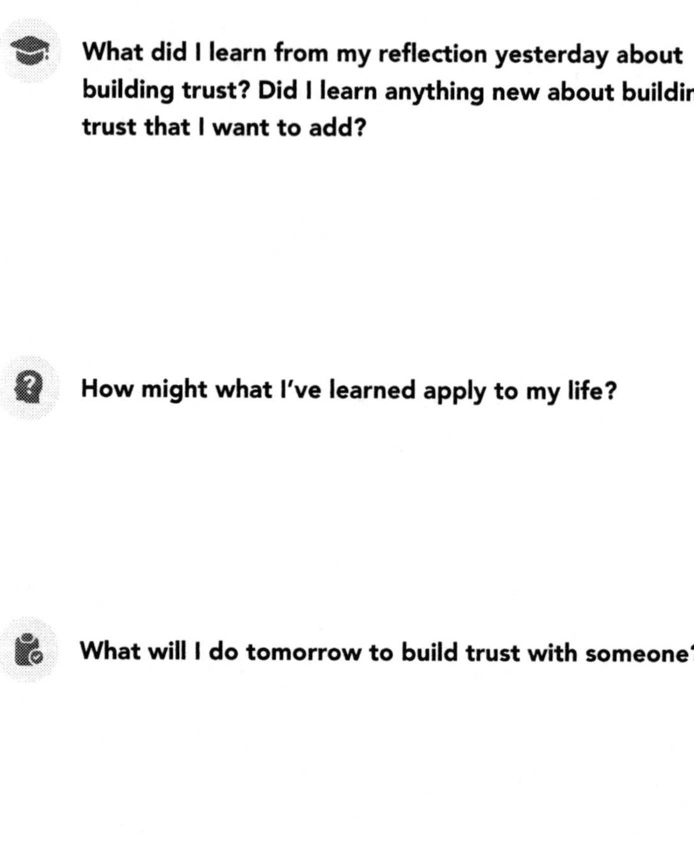

What did I learn from my reflection yesterday about building trust? Did I learn anything new about building trust that I want to add?

How might what I've learned apply to my life?

What will I do tomorrow to build trust with someone?

Reflection:

DAY 14

What did I learn from my reflection yesterday about building trust? Did I learn anything new about building trust that I want to add?

How might what I've learned apply to my life?

What will I do tomorrow to build trust with someone?

Reflection:

> *"Trust costs nothing and expands everything."*
> *—Farmer Able in* Farmer Able, *by Art Barter*

"To be trusted is a greater compliment than being loved."
—George Macdonald

Your Visualization Exercise — Building Trust

My visualization for building trust is a school bus. After I leave home in the morning, I pass the bus stop for an elementary school. We have been working with a local school district to improve trust in their organization after a survey they took showed decline in students' trust as they got older. In elementary school, the students' trust level started out okay; in middle school they experienced a decline in trust; in high school the trust was even lower. We are raising a generation that doesn't trust the world around them. The school bus I see every day reminds me to build trust with others in my life.

Close your eyes and picture what building trust looks like to you. This will be the picture that will represent building trust for you. Make sure it is a picture of something you do every day.

Close your eyes again and visualize your picture of serving first, and then building trust.

Write your true life visualization of what building trust looks like to you.

Chapter 4

Behavior No. 3 —
LIVE YOUR VALUES

> *"When your values are clear to you, making decisions becomes easier." —Roy Disney*

When my wife Lori and I bought the radio company in 2004, we were in a turnaround situation. We believed in the future of the company, but it was struggling. And we wanted to change the whole culture of the company to focus on serving first. We hired an outside consultant to come in and help the executive team, through some offsite meetings, decide what type of company we wanted to be and how we wanted to do business. We created the mission and purpose during those meetings, and we identified the values that would define how we behave as a company. We all agreed that, as a private company, we wanted to create a completely different culture than we had had as a public company.

These are the building blocks we used to define our company's values:

- They would be our ethical and moral compass.
- They would reflect the ideals and ethics of our leaders.
- They would drive our decision-making processes on a daily basis.
- When things got tough, we still had to make decisions that were consistent with the values.
- They would be used internally and externally (with our customers, suppliers, and anyone else we did business with).
- They would be best when few in number and high in meaning.

Based on those foundational building blocks, these are the values we came up with:

1. Our families come first
2. Honor and serve others
3. Conduct ourselves ethically and with integrity
4. Honest and trustworthy
5. Uncompromising in our values

These values are the cornerstone of all our activity, and every employee is held accountable to them.

I recommend you post your company's values so they are visible throughout your organization, but that's only a small part of it. You have to create an environment where everyone in the organization can live your values. It's more than just telling your employees what you want them to do. When you present your values, you'll have opportunities to mentor and coach. We call those "teachable moments." That's when you sit down with people and help them understand why you do what you do and why the values are so important. The values have to drive their behavior, and that only happens when they understand the purpose behind them.

Take the values off the wall and plant them, water them, and fertilize them. Make sure they're alive and well throughout your organization and not just pretty words on a plaque hanging on the wall.

DAY 1

What I've learned today about living my values:

How might what I've learned apply to my life?

What will I do tomorrow to live my values?

Reflection:

DAY 2

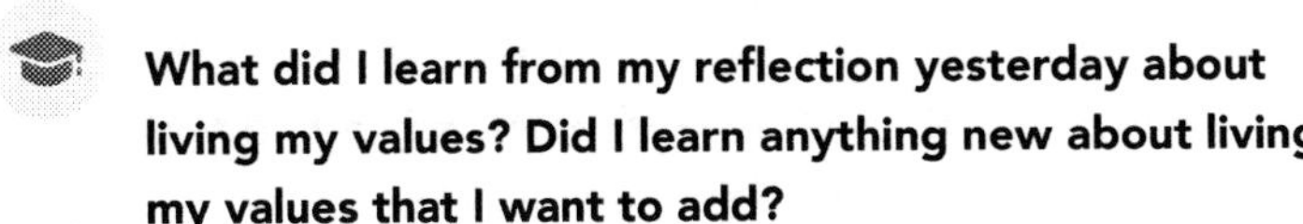

What did I learn from my reflection yesterday about living my values? Did I learn anything new about living my values that I want to add?

How might what I've learned apply to my life?

What will I do tomorrow to live my values?

Reflection:

DAY 3

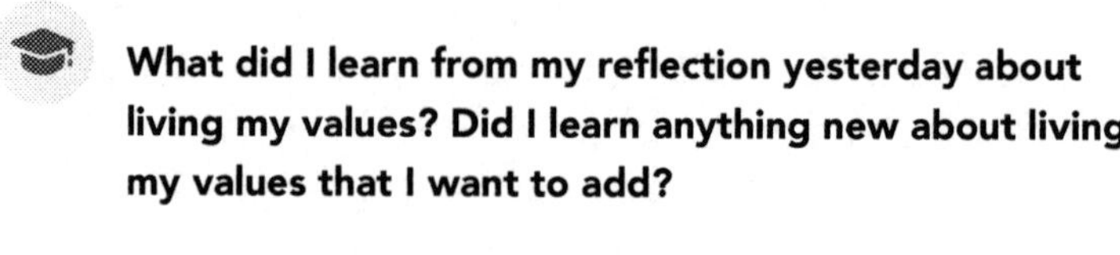

What did I learn from my reflection yesterday about living my values? Did I learn anything new about living my values that I want to add?

How might what I've learned apply to my life?

What will I do tomorrow to live my values?

Reflection:

DAY 4

What did I learn from my reflection yesterday about living my values? Did I learn anything new about living my values that I want to add?

How might what I've learned apply to my life?

What will I do tomorrow to live my values?

Reflection:

"Your life is your statement to the world representing your values, your beliefs, your dreams." —David Arenson

DAY 5

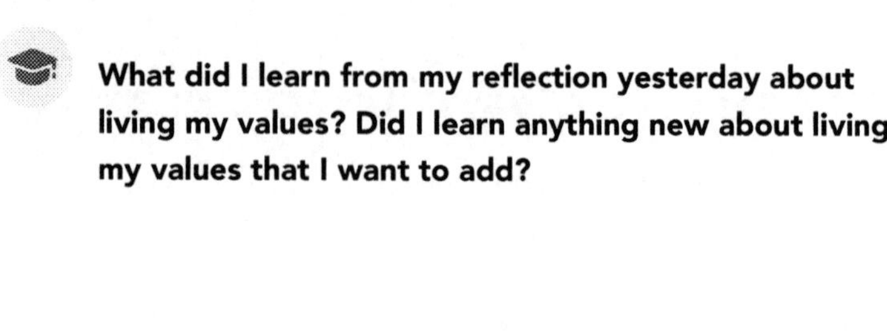

What did I learn from my reflection yesterday about living my values? Did I learn anything new about living my values that I want to add?

How might what I've learned apply to my life?

What will I do tomorrow to live my values?

Reflection:

DAY 6

What did I learn from my reflection yesterday about living my values? Did I learn anything new about living my values that I want to add?

How might what I've learned apply to my life?

What will I do tomorrow to live my values?

Reflection:

DAY 7

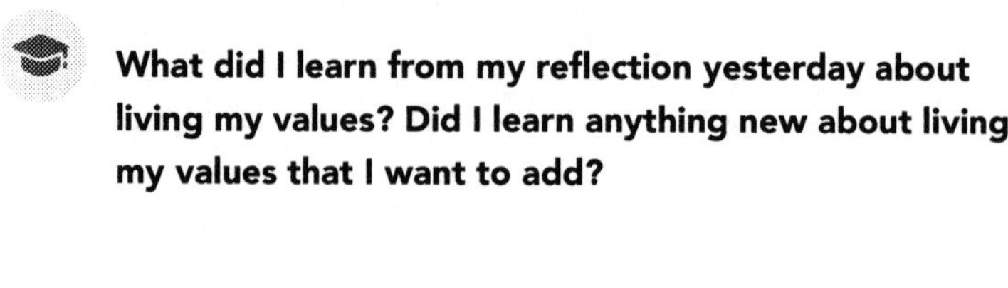

What did I learn from my reflection yesterday about living my values? Did I learn anything new about living my values that I want to add?

How might what I've learned apply to my life?

What will I do tomorrow to live my values?

Reflection:

"Living in a way that reflects one's values is not just about what you do, it is also about how you do things." —Deborah Day

DAY 8

What did I learn from my reflection yesterday about living my values? Did I learn anything new about living my values that I want to add?

How might what I've learned apply to my life?

What will I do tomorrow to live my values?

Reflection:

DAY 9

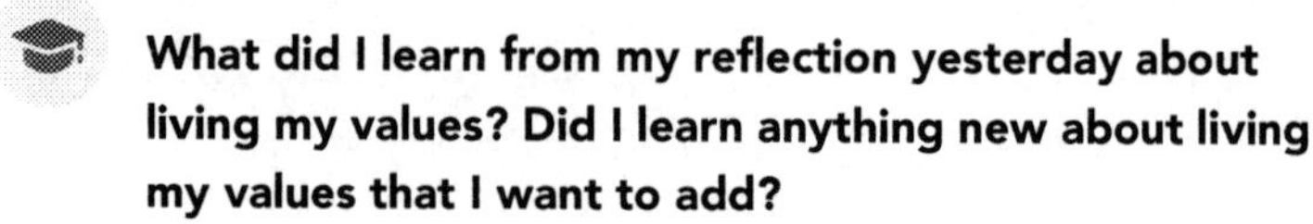

What did I learn from my reflection yesterday about living my values? Did I learn anything new about living my values that I want to add?

How might what I've learned apply to my life?

What will I do tomorrow to live my values?

Reflection:

DAY 10

What did I learn from my reflection yesterday about living my values? Did I learn anything new about living my values that I want to add?

How might what I've learned apply to my life?

What will I do tomorrow to live my values?

Reflection:

"How you get results is more important that the results themselves."
—Art Barter

DAY 11

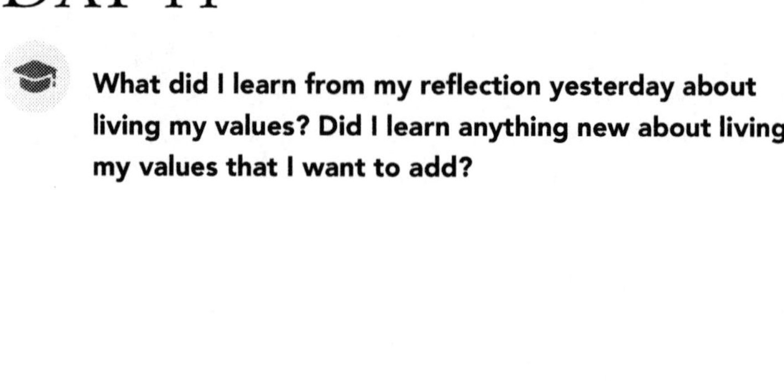

What did I learn from my reflection yesterday about living my values? Did I learn anything new about living my values that I want to add?

How might what I've learned apply to my life?

What will I do tomorrow to live my values?

Reflection:

"To feel more fulfilled your actions and activities need to be in alignment with what you deem important." —Deborah Day

DAY 12

What did I learn from my reflection yesterday about living my values? Did I learn anything new about living my values that I want to add?

How might what I've learned apply to my life?

What will I do tomorrow to live my values?

Reflection:

DAY 13

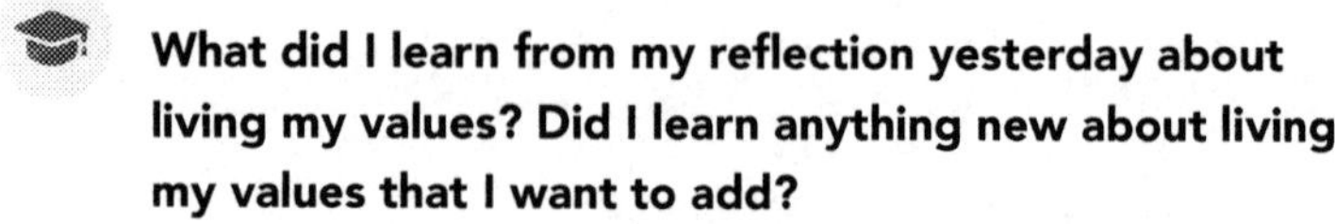

What did I learn from my reflection yesterday about living my values? Did I learn anything new about living my values that I want to add?

How might what I've learned apply to my life?

What will I do tomorrow to live my values?

Reflection:

DAY 14

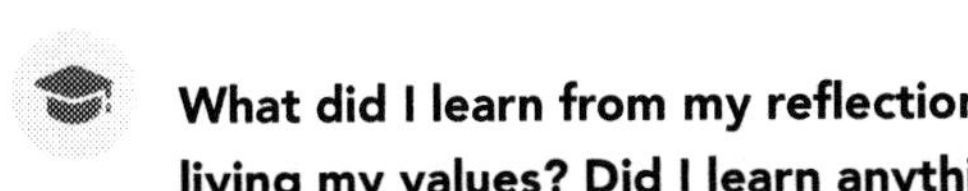

What did I learn from my reflection yesterday about living my values? Did I learn anything new about living my values that I want to add?

How might what I've learned apply to my life?

What will I do tomorrow to live my values?

Reflection:

"Values aren't buses... They're not supposed to get you anywhere. They're supposed to define who you are." —Jennifer Crusie

Your Visualization Exercise — Living Your Values

My visualization of living my values is getting on the freeway. After I make coffee for Lori and drive past the school bus stop on my way to work, I get on the freeway. The on-ramp I use is long, and I have a chance to look at the traffic flow and see who is in the slow lane that I will need to cooperate with to enter en masse. It reminds me that I need to live my values: trust others, not get upset at anyone, be honest by using my turn signal and be respectful by thanking the driver who lets me in. Sometimes I need to slow down to enter the flow of traffic safely. We are all driving vehicles that average 3,000 to 6,000 lbs. in weight, and drive an average of 60 to 70 miles an hour. It's important to live our values on the freeway, or we risk accident, injury or even death. Living my values as I get on the freeway has a definite influence on the remainder of my day.

Close your eyes and picture what living your values looks like to you. This will be the picture that will represent how you live your values. Make sure it is a picture of something you do every day.

Close your eyes again and visualize your picture of serving first and your picture of building trust; now think about your picture of living your values. Spend a few minutes thinking about your journey and your pictures of the first three behaviors.

Write your true life visualization of what living your values looks like to you.

Chapter 5

Behavior No. 4 — LISTEN TO UNDERSTAND

> *"Most people do not listen with the intent to understand; they listen with the intent to reply."*
> *—Stephen R. Covey,* The 7 Habits of Highly Effective People: Powerful Lessons in Personal Change

Most of us are not natural servant leaders. I believe it is a learned behavior, just as listening is a learned discipline.

Early on in our implementation at Datron, our management team identified 10 traits they believed servant leaders should have, and one of those was to be a good listener. At the time, we all agreed to a 360 evaluation in which we assessed each other on those 10 traits. We also agreed we would share the results with each other and commit to improving the two traits we were rated the lowest on.

I read the results of my survey about 6 p.m. on a Friday, and I quickly determined there must be something wrong with the survey. I knew the questions could not have been structured properly, which of course had made the results totally inaccurate. When I got home, my wife Lori could tell something was bothering me. I shared with her that the survey was wrong and we were going to have to invest more money to start over. She said, "Why do you feel that way?" I told her it was because I was rated the lowest in listening, and I knew that was wrong. Without missing a beat or even looking up from what she was doing, she said, "Tell me something I don't already know." I had gone home looking for support for my feelings that the survey was wrong, and what I got was confirmation it was accurate—I was not a good listener. It was not a good weekend!

As a result of that experience, I started studying listening, and what I learned is that listening is actually a form of love. If I really cared about others and about being their servant leader, I had to learn how to listen. If I really wanted to serve others, I had to learn to listen to understand...first, before I could offer or provide any help.

Listening involves a more sophisticated mental process than just hearing. If you have children, you know you can have conversations with them when they're listening to you, but they're not hearing what you have to say. As adults, we do the same thing. Listening demands energy and discipline, because it requires that we consciously decide not to have a debate in our minds about what we're going to say next. We have to focus on understanding what's being said instead of doing something else or thinking about our next appointment. Listening and understanding go hand in hand.

There are several barriers to being a good listener:

- Selective listening: hearing only what you want to hear and tuning out the rest
- The tendency to interrupt: preferring to hear your own voice over another's
- Fear that you might have to change your opinion because you might be wrong
- The tendency to jump to conclusions
- Listening to respond: thinking about a response rather than actively listening
- The tendency to judge or evaluate before fully understanding what you've heard: not having all the information before make a decision

Here are some techniques that help us overcome those barriers and become good listeners:

- Be aware of non-verbal and verbal messages (like crossing your arms or leaning back in your chair) that give the indication you're not interested in what the person is saying.
- Shut out external distractions (like your phone or computer) and focus.
- Listen with an open mind. Listening to understand requires a different mindset.
- Do not interrupt. Let the person make his or her point.
- Be sensitive to the emotions behind the discussion. A large part of the reactions we get from people have nothing to do with the communication; it has to do with an experience they've had, maybe with another company or another leader, or perhaps something that's going on in their lives.

I often tell my leaders to "listen from the heart." When you listen from the heart, you put your focus on other people and their needs. Listening from the heart involves creating a safe environment for that communication. When you listen from the heart, you want to ask the person two key questions: "Help me to understand," and "Tell me more." Then keep asking those questions until you really do understand.

How well you listen affects the performance of your organization. If you don't listen and understand what's going on, you may end up going down a path you really don't want to go down, spending resources that don't fix the problem.

DAY 1

What did I learn about listening to understand?

How might what I've learned apply to my life?

What will I do tomorrow to listen to understand?

Reflection:

"One of the most sincere forms of respect is actually listening to what another has to say." —Bryant H. McGill

DAY 2

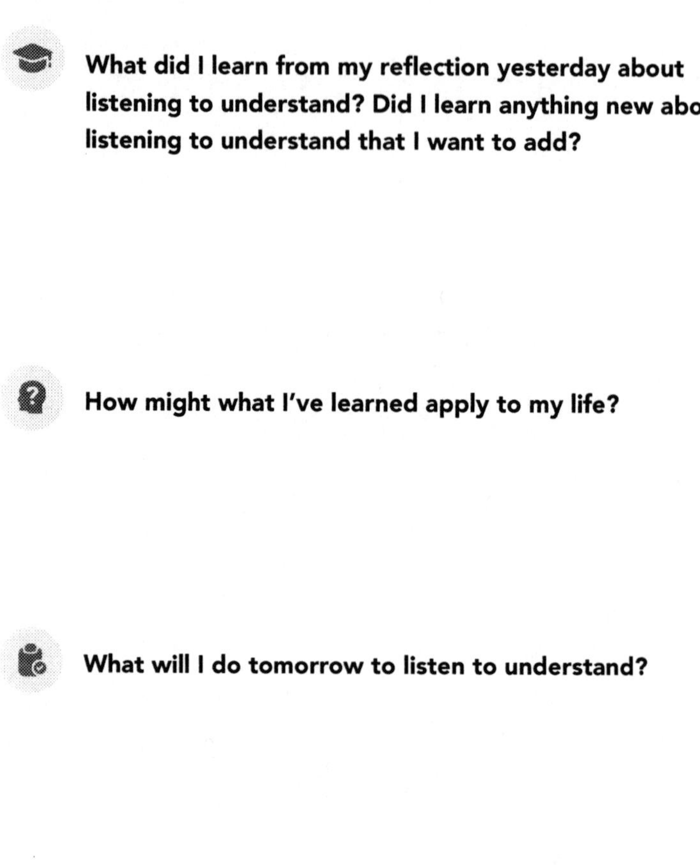

What did I learn from my reflection yesterday about listening to understand? Did I learn anything new about listening to understand that I want to add?

How might what I've learned apply to my life?

What will I do tomorrow to listen to understand?

Reflection:

DAY 3

What did I learn from my reflection yesterday about listening to understand? Did I learn anything new about listening to understand that I want to add?

How might what I've learned apply to my life?

What will I do tomorrow to listen to understand?

Reflection:

DAY 4

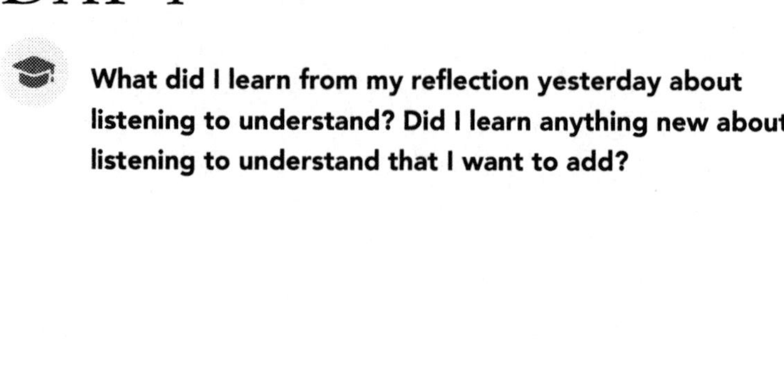

What did I learn from my reflection yesterday about listening to understand? Did I learn anything new about listening to understand that I want to add?

How might what I've learned apply to my life?

What will I do tomorrow to listen to understand?

Reflection:

DAY 5

What did I learn from my reflection yesterday about listening to understand? Did I learn anything new about listening to understand that I want to add?

How might what I've learned apply to my life?

What will I do tomorrow to listen to understand?

Reflection:

"We have two ears and one tongue so that we would listen more and talk less." —Diogenes

DAY 6

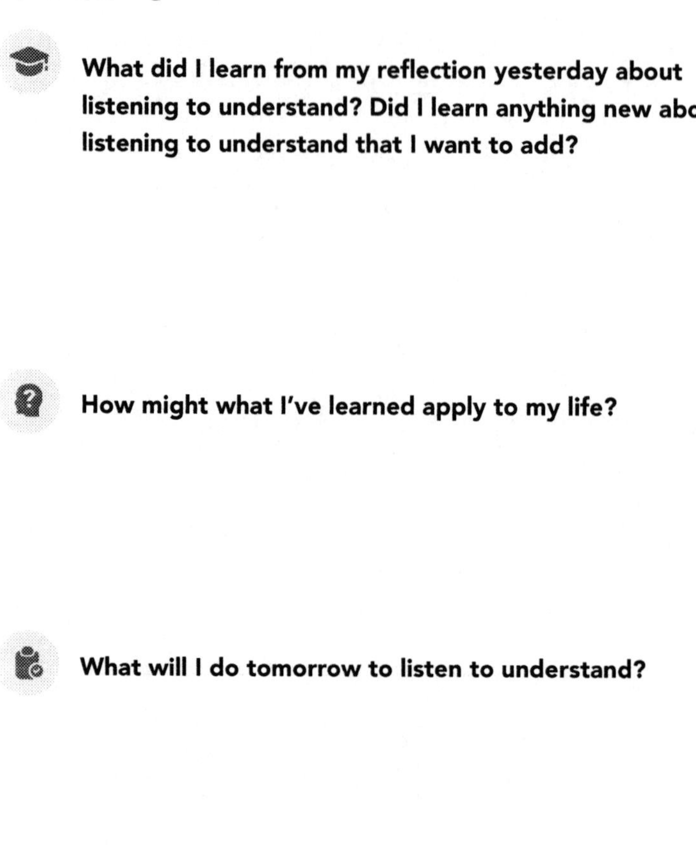

What did I learn from my reflection yesterday about listening to understand? Did I learn anything new about listening to understand that I want to add?

How might what I've learned apply to my life?

What will I do tomorrow to listen to understand?

Reflection:

DAY 7

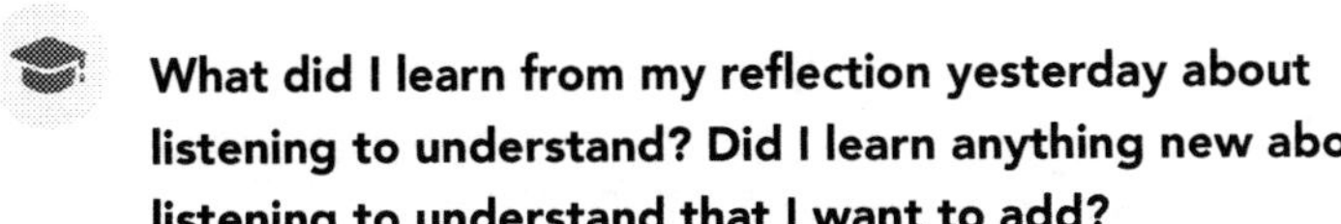

What did I learn from my reflection yesterday about listening to understand? Did I learn anything new about listening to understand that I want to add?

How might what I've learned apply to my life?

What will I do tomorrow to listen to understand?

Reflection:

"You cannot truly listen to anyone and do anything else at the same time." —M. Scott Peck

DAY 8

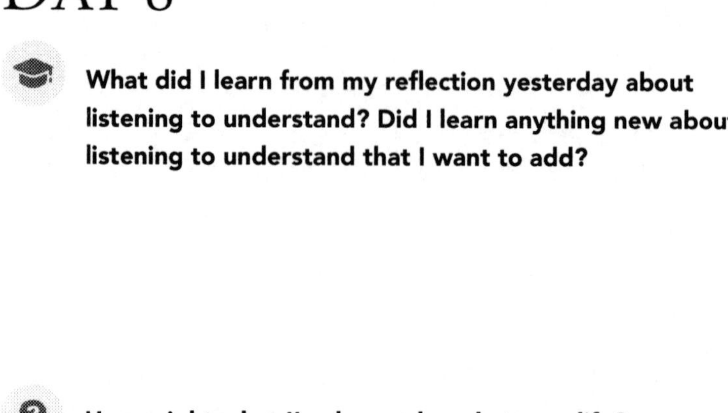

What did I learn from my reflection yesterday about listening to understand? Did I learn anything new about listening to understand that I want to add?

How might what I've learned apply to my life?

What will I do tomorrow to listen to understand?

Reflection:

DAY 9

What did I learn from my reflection yesterday about listening to understand? Did I learn anything new about listening to understand that I want to add?

How might what I've learned apply to my life?

What will I do tomorrow to listen to understand?

Reflection:

DAY 10

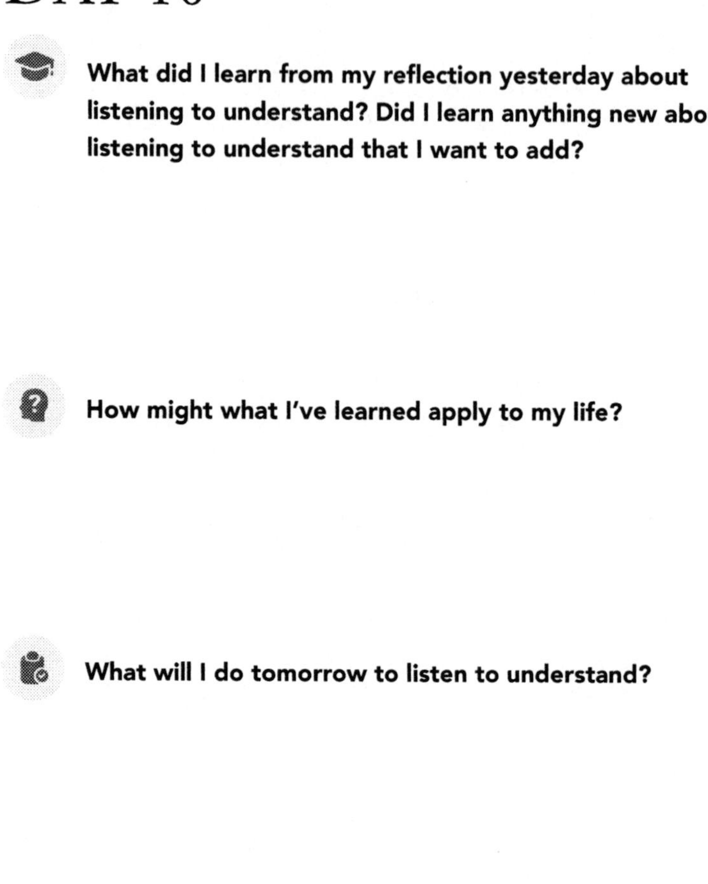

What did I learn from my reflection yesterday about listening to understand? Did I learn anything new about listening to understand that I want to add?

How might what I've learned apply to my life?

What will I do tomorrow to listen to understand?

Reflection:

"Most of the successful people I've known are the ones who do more listening than talking." —*Bernard Baruch*

DAY 11

What did I learn from my reflection yesterday about listening to understand? Did I learn anything new about listening to understand that I want to add?

How might what I've learned apply to my life?

What will I do tomorrow to listen to understand?

Reflection:

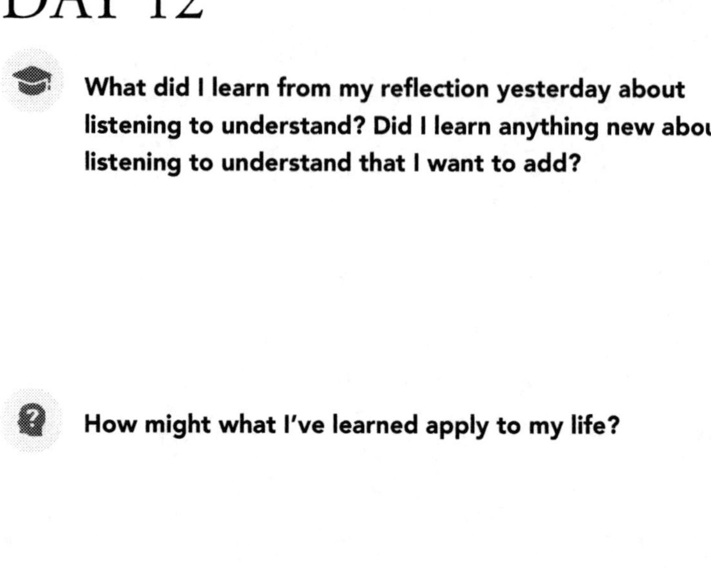

DAY 12

What did I learn from my reflection yesterday about listening to understand? Did I learn anything new about listening to understand that I want to add?

How might what I've learned apply to my life?

What will I do tomorrow to listen to understand?

Reflection:

DAY 13

What did I learn from my reflection yesterday about listening to understand? Did I learn anything new about listening to understand that I want to add?

How might what I've learned apply to my life?

What will I do tomorrow to listen to understand?

Reflection:

"The art of conversation lies in listening." —Malcom Forbes

DAY 14

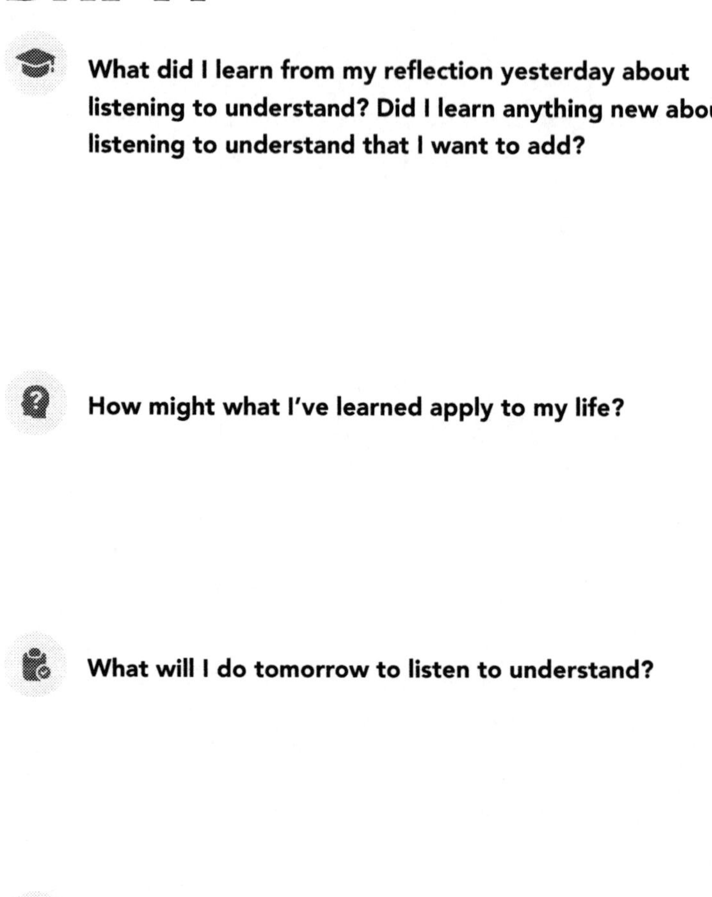

What did I learn from my reflection yesterday about listening to understand? Did I learn anything new about listening to understand that I want to add?

How might what I've learned apply to my life?

What will I do tomorrow to listen to understand?

Reflection:

"Listening is being able to be changed by the other person."
—Alan Alda

Your Visualization Exercise — Listening to Understand

My visualization of listening to understand is talking on my cell phone on my way to work. After I get on the freeway, I usually have a conversation with someone in our offices located outside of California or overseas. (Yes, I have hands-free in my car; thank you for asking.) Talking on the cell phone while the car is moving requires concentration. Depending on where I am calling, there may be a delay in the actual voice transmission. I find myself consciously listening until the other party stops talking.

To really understand what is being said by another person, I focus on two questions: "Tell me more" and "Help me understand." Asking these two questions helps me make sure I understand what is being said. I continue asking until I have a clear understanding of what the other person is saying. Being a good listener shows you care.

Close your eyes and picture what listening to understand looks like to you. This will be the picture that will represent how you listen to others. Make sure it is a picture of something you do every day.

Close your eyes again and visualize your picture of serving first, building trust, and living your values; now add your picture of listening to understand. Spend a few minutes thinking about your journey and your pictures of the first four behaviors.

Write your true life visualization of what listening to understand looks like to you.

Chapter 6

Behavior No. 5 — THINK ABOUT YOUR THINKING

"Thinking: the talking of the soul with itself." —Plato

"Thinking is the hardest work there is, which is probably the reason why so few engage in it." —Henry Ford

Thinking about our thinking is the process of observing and questioning how and why we think the way we do. It's a very important part of the personal change we go through in our transformation to servant leadership.

To change our mindset, we have to think about our thinking. Understanding our thinking and why we react in certain ways makes us a much more empathetic leader, and a better follower as well. When we can recognize negative thoughts, we can turn them around, which will result in an improvement in our performance and in our ability to influence other people.

Thinking about our thinking can also change the way we do our work and the way we lead. For example, if someone comes to us with an urgent request for our help and we're already up to our eyeballs with work, we could take the victim stance and probably think of a very negative response that includes "woe is me." But when we stop to think about what we're thinking, we can say, "Maybe I should think about this a different way. How can I make a difference in this situation?" That's the difference between useful and non-useful thoughts. Useful thoughts take us out of the role of being the victim and help us go forward in a positive way. It's a matter of slowing down, thinking about the thoughts we're having and reframing the non-useful thoughts into useful thoughts.

Probably the most important action a servant leader can take is to allow time to withdraw and reflect. For most of us, our schedules are so busy that we have to force ourselves to make this time. If we have a long commute home, that's an excellent time to reflect and think about the events of our day and about how we thought during each of them.

Obviously, thinking is automatic and we can't stop it; but we can observe it, and the more we practice observing and changing our thinking, the easier it gets. Observing our thinking gives us an opportunity to take note of our ego, which is probably the first thing we come up against—and need to change—when we're making that mind shift to serving people first. In essence, we observe and question our way of thinking until we can get it to line up with our servant leadership values.

As a leader, we have to be a positive role model for the people we serve. If we can't adjust our thinking to useful thoughts, how will we ever project a positive image to those we influence who are looking to us for direction? Our negative thoughts can have an effect on how we represent our organization, and we can even become disconnected from our company's values. It's difficult to represent those values well if we're not thinking about the way we think.

Our thinking may even limit our ability to trust others, especially if we're forming judgmental opinions that are not based on facts. When mistrust is present, it's difficult to have a good working relationship; our work—and the work of everyone around us—suffers. At that point, it's difficult to see through the servant-leader lens.

Here are some questions that can help us self-correct as we're thinking about our thinking in any situation:

- What is going on inside of me at this moment?
- Am I feeling self-serving emotions?

- Is my ego getting in the way?
- Am I willing to listen to honest feedback from someone I trust?
- Am I willing to consider my responsibility in any situation?

Today is your starting point for thinking about your thinking. I believe after you've practiced it and journaled about it for the next 14 days, you'll be well on your way to changing your behavior.

DAY 1

What did I learn about thinking about my thinking?

How might what I've learned apply to my life?

What will I do tomorrow to think about my thinking?

Reflection:

DAY 2

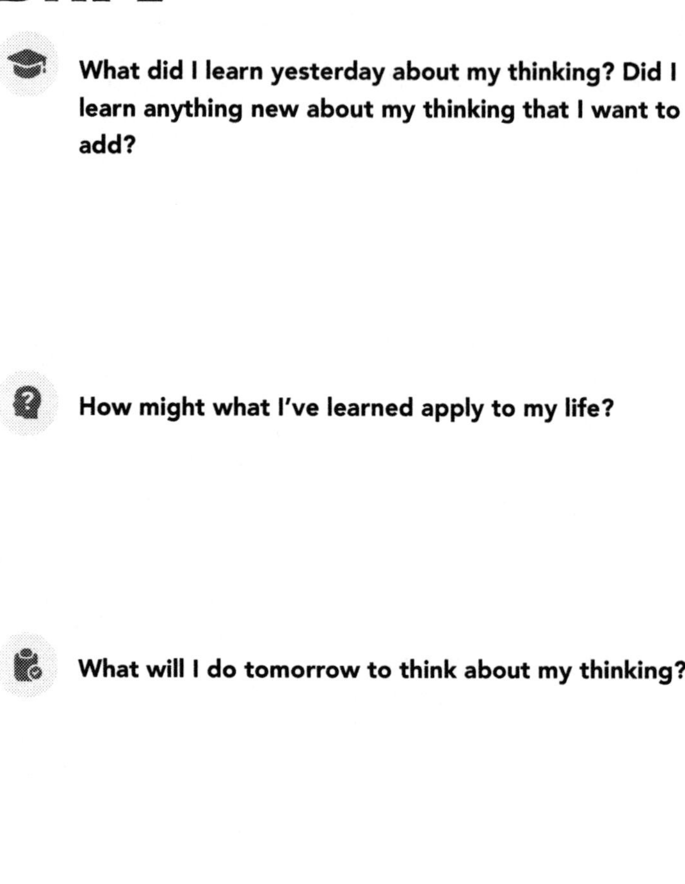

What did I learn yesterday about my thinking? Did I learn anything new about my thinking that I want to add?

How might what I've learned apply to my life?

What will I do tomorrow to think about my thinking?

Reflection:

"We cannot solve our problems with the same thinking we used when we created them." —Albert Einstein

DAY 3

What did I learn yesterday about my thinking? Did I learn anything new about my thinking that I want to add?

How might what I've learned apply to my life?

What will I do tomorrow to think about my thinking?

Reflection:

DAY 4

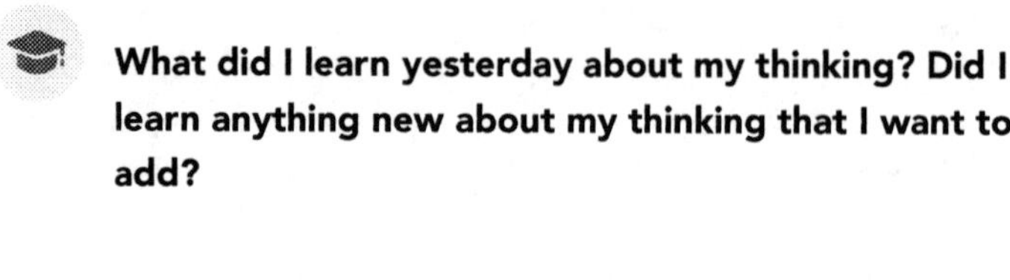

What did I learn yesterday about my thinking? Did I learn anything new about my thinking that I want to add?

How might what I've learned apply to my life?

What will I do tomorrow to think about my thinking?

Reflection:

DAY 5

What did I learn yesterday about my thinking? Did I learn anything new about my thinking that I want to add?

How might what I've learned apply to my life?

What will I do tomorrow to think about my thinking?

Reflection:

DAY 6

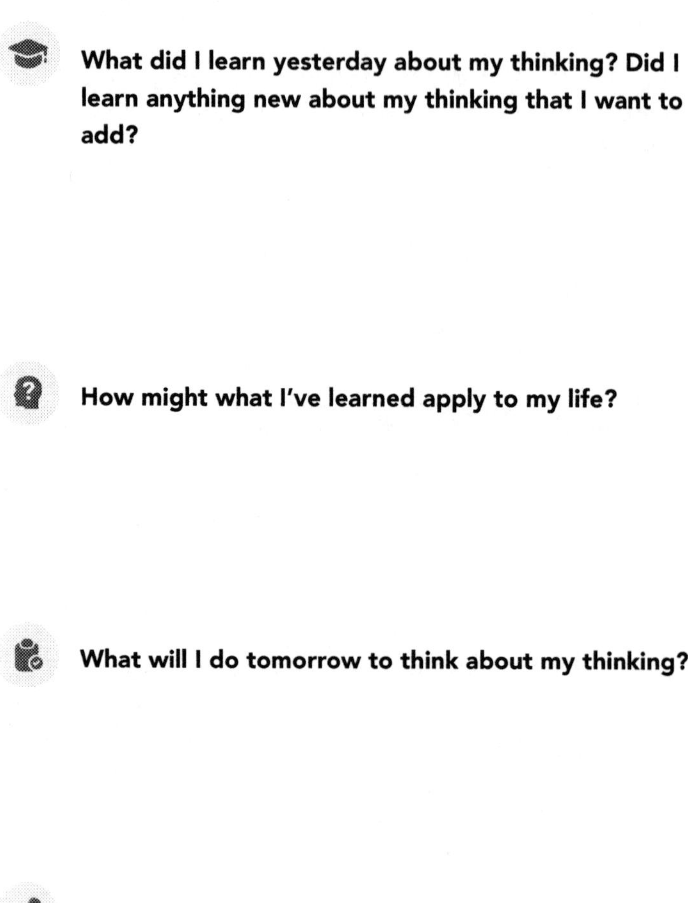

What did I learn yesterday about my thinking? Did I learn anything new about my thinking that I want to add?

How might what I've learned apply to my life?

What will I do tomorrow to think about my thinking?

Reflection:

"Creative thinking inspires ideas. Ideas inspire change."
—Barbara Januszkiewicz

DAY 7

What did I learn yesterday about my thinking? Did I learn anything new about my thinking that I want to add?

How might what I've learned apply to my life?

What will I do tomorrow to think about my thinking?

Reflection:

DAY 8

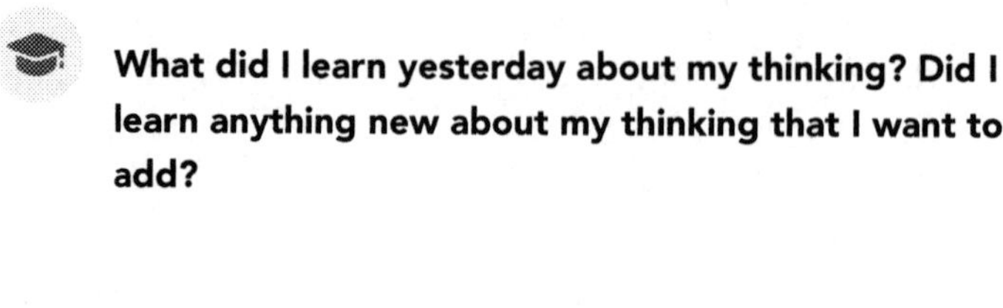

What did I learn yesterday about my thinking? Did I learn anything new about my thinking that I want to add?

How might what I've learned apply to my life?

What will I do tomorrow to think about my thinking?

Reflection:

DAY 9

What did I learn yesterday about my thinking? Did I learn anything new about my thinking that I want to add?

How might what I've learned apply to my life?

What will I do tomorrow to think about my thinking?

Reflection:

"How we think shows through in how we act. Attitudes are mirrors of the mind. They reflect thinking." —*David Joseph Schwartz*

DAY 10

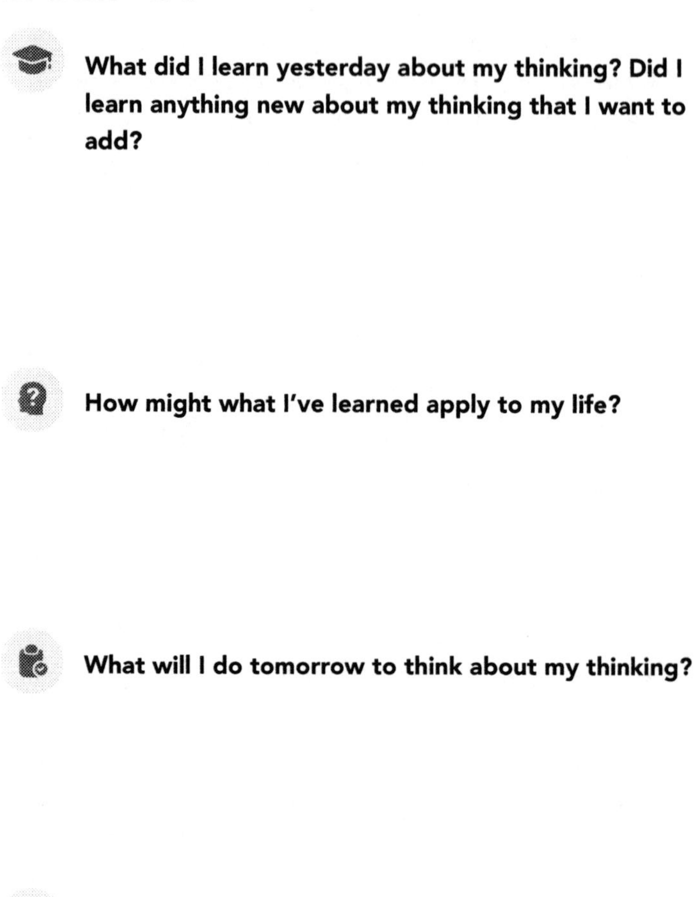

What did I learn yesterday about my thinking? Did I learn anything new about my thinking that I want to add?

How might what I've learned apply to my life?

What will I do tomorrow to think about my thinking?

Reflection:

"I don't think we spend enough time in reflection and introspection. We don't know who we are as individuals in this culture anymore."
—Naomi Judd

DAY 11

What did I learn yesterday about my thinking? Did I learn anything new about my thinking that I want to add?

How might what I've learned apply to my life?

What will I do tomorrow to think about my thinking?

Reflection:

DAY 12

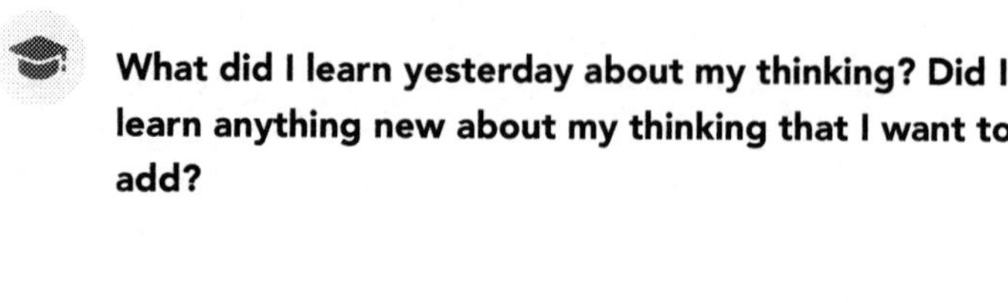

What did I learn yesterday about my thinking? Did I learn anything new about my thinking that I want to add?

How might what I've learned apply to my life?

What will I do tomorrow to think about my thinking?

Reflection:

"You are today where your thoughts have brought you; you will be tomorrow where your thoughts take you." —*James Allen*

DAY 13

What did I learn yesterday about my thinking? Did I learn anything new about my thinking that I want to add?

How might what I've learned apply to my life?

What will I do tomorrow to think about my thinking?

Reflection:

"Thought creates character."—Annie Besant

DAY 14

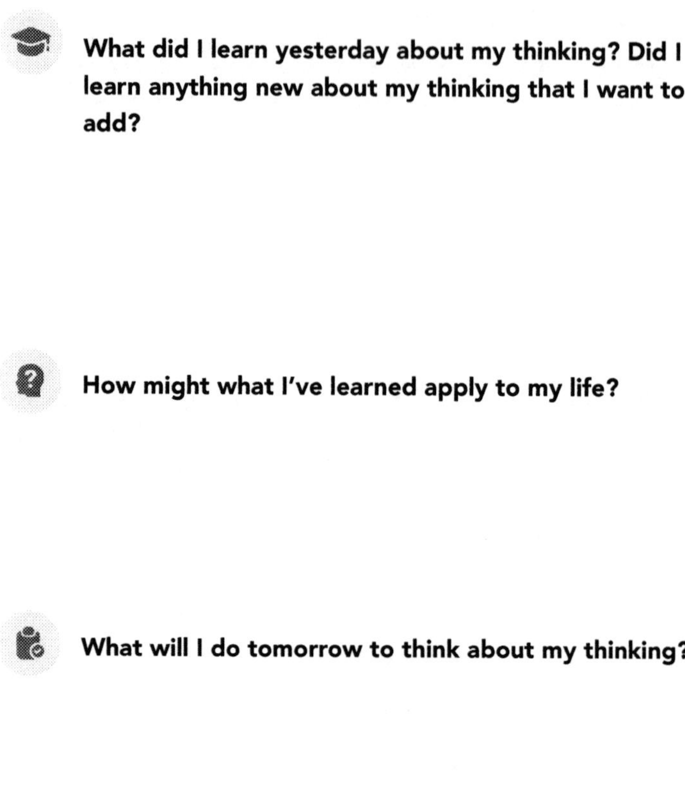

What did I learn yesterday about my thinking? Did I learn anything new about my thinking that I want to add?

How might what I've learned apply to my life?

What will I do tomorrow to think about my thinking?

Reflection:

"Remember, happiness doesn't depend upon who you are or what you have; it depends solely upon what you think." —Dale Carnegie

Your Visualization Exercise — Thinking About Your Thinking

My visualization of thinking about my thinking is that period of time in my car on my way to work between getting off my cell phone and actually arriving at work. During this time, I think about the day ahead. It's not the only time I spend reflecting and thinking. In fact, I find myself today spending more time in thought than ever before in my career. Change occurs daily, and the only way I know to deal with all the change is to have some quiet time to consider, think about, and reflect on all that is before me. I believe every good leader spends time alone. We need this time to clear our thoughts and focus on what is important. It allows us time to ensure our priorities are in order, our decisions are not surrounded by emotions, and we are properly serving those around us. Take the time today to find a spot you can call your own and spend 10 minutes thinking about where you are and where you want to be.

Close your eyes and picture what thinking about your thinking looks like to you. This will be the picture that will represent how you think about your thinking. Make sure it is a picture of something you do every day.

Close your eyes again and visualize your picture of serving first, then your picture of building trust, then your picture of living your values, then listening to understand, and finally thinking about your thinking. Spend a few minutes thinking about your journey and your pictures of the first five behaviors.

Write your true life visualization of what thinking about your thinking looks like to you.

Chapter 7

Behavior No. 6 —

ADD VALUE TO OTHERS

> *"What counts in life is not the mere fact that we have lived. It is what difference we have made to the lives of others that will determine the significance of the life we lead."*
> *—Nelson Mandela*

Have you ever benefited from someone's contribution toward you? We all have experiences where someone has helped us be better at who we are or what we do. In my case, there are several individuals over my career who have helped me believe in myself. Later in life, I've had the fortune of working with my good friends Ken Blanchard, Stephen M.R. Covey, John Maxwell, Ron Jensen and Werner Jacobsen. Each has mentored me and compelled me to improve as an individual and as a leader.

A leader who consistently adds value to others is a leader who has a mindset of thinking about and investing time in others, who listens to and empathizes with those they influence, and who helps them improve in both their individual and team work. This type of leader looks for win-win situations for everyone: the individual, the team, and the organization.

As servant leaders, we inspire and equip those we influence, and that includes everyone around us. The best way to influence others is to provide help and assistance on a consistent basis. Once people know you care about them—genuinely, from the heart—they will respond in ways that will amaze you. Leaders can set audacious goals, but they can only reach those goals as long as they invest in their people and help them succeed. When people are succeeding, the organization is succeeding.

One of the best ways to add value to people in your organization is to help them use the knowledge they have. We all have knowledge inside of us, and most of us would like to put that knowledge to use for the good of the organization we work for. Others throughout our organization feel the same way. They are waiting for leaders to use the knowledge they have for the good of the organization.

Another way to add value within the organization is to communicate and share information with everyone. Be truthful about where you are in the business, and that includes the successes you're having as well as the struggles you may be going through. It's easy for leaders to share and add value when everything's going great. But when you're struggling, it's very difficult to comfortably share that information. It's important to be positive about where you are as a company, but don't try to spin the story or add anything extra to make it look better.

Investing in the education of your people is another excellent way to add value to them. That's a value they can take with them for the rest of their lives. Adding value to others by investing your time and money shows you really care about them. We also invest our time in mentoring and coaching.

I believe one of the best ways to add value is to help your people learn from their mistakes. Everyone makes mistakes. When that happens, don't reach into your toolbox and bring out your hammer; instead, bring your heart out of your tool box and help that person learn from his or her mistake. Ken Blanchard taught me to never punish a learner. Let mistakes become teachable moments.

Think about who adds value to your life. And more importantly, how do you add value to others? Besides the ones I've already listed, there are many ways we can add value. Here are a few examples: Create something someone can use; inspire and equip someone to take action; extend a helping hand; teach someone to do something, show them a better way, or provide a new perspective; listen in a time of need; or just be there for someone when they need it—extend grace, show them your heart, or serve them before yourself.

How will you add value to others in your life—your spouse, your children, your co-workers, and others you influence? How will you add value to those less fortunate than you in our society? Only you can answer those questions.

Enjoy your journey. In the next 14 days, you may be surprised at what you discover.

DAY 1

What did I learn about adding value to others?

How might what I've learned apply to my life?

What will I do tomorrow to add value to others?

Reflection:

"Never get tired of doing little things for others. Sometimes, those little things occupy the biggest part of their hearts." —Unknown

DAY 2

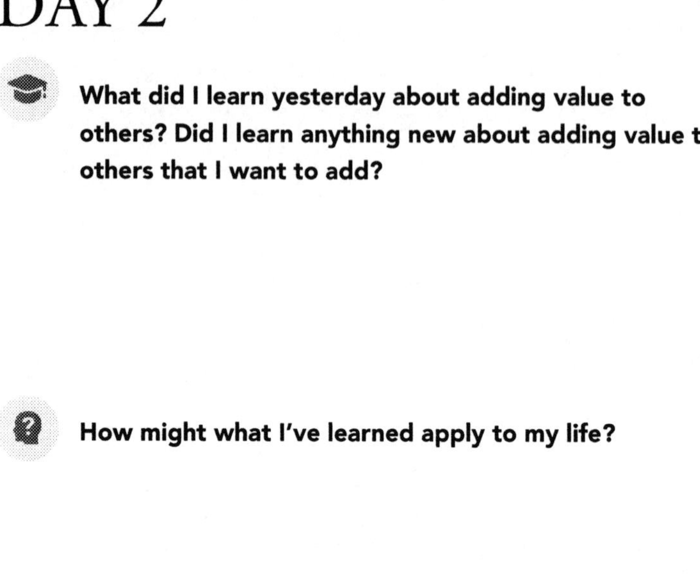

What did I learn yesterday about adding value to others? Did I learn anything new about adding value to others that I want to add?

How might what I've learned apply to my life?

What will I do tomorrow to add value to others?

Reflection:

DAY 3

What did I learn yesterday about adding value to others? Did I learn anything new about adding value to others that I want to add?

How might what I've learned apply to my life?

What will I do tomorrow to add value to others?

Reflection:

DAY 4

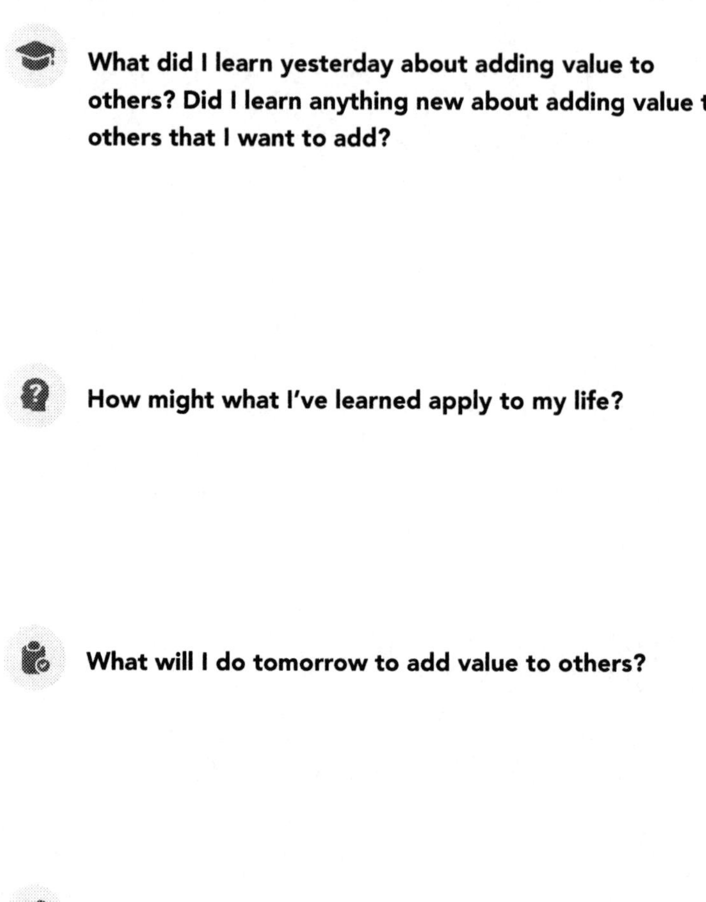

What did I learn yesterday about adding value to others? Did I learn anything new about adding value to others that I want to add?

How might what I've learned apply to my life?

What will I do tomorrow to add value to others?

Reflection:

"As we work to create light for others, we naturally light our own way."—Mary Anne Radmacher

DAY 5

What did I learn yesterday about adding value to others? Did I learn anything new about adding value to others that I want to add?

How might what I've learned apply to my life?

What will I do tomorrow to add value to others?

Reflection:

DAY 6

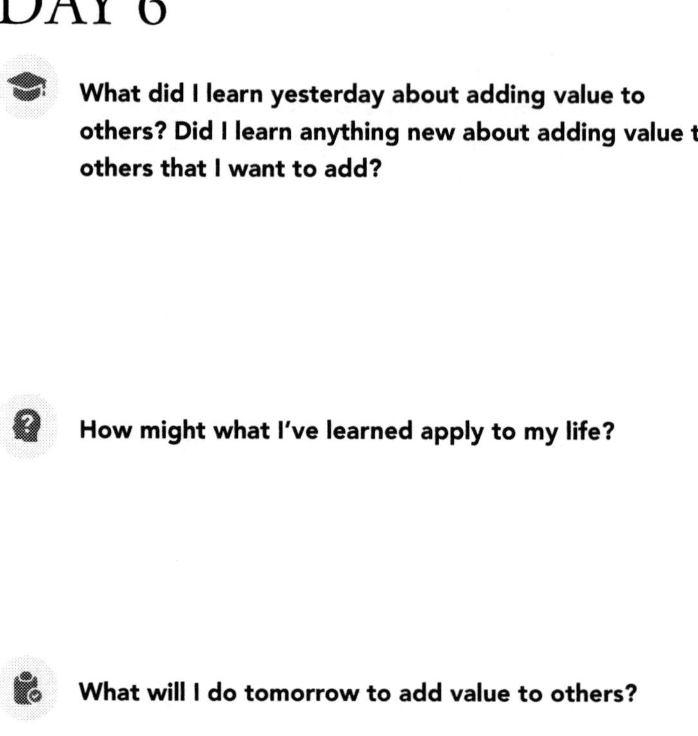

What did I learn yesterday about adding value to others? Did I learn anything new about adding value to others that I want to add?

How might what I've learned apply to my life?

What will I do tomorrow to add value to others?

Reflection:

"I feel that the greatest reward for doing is the opportunity to do more." —Dr. Jonas Salk

DAY 7

What did I learn yesterday about adding value to others? Did I learn anything new about adding value to others that I want to add?

How might what I've learned apply to my life?

What will I do tomorrow to add value to others?

Reflection:

DAY 8

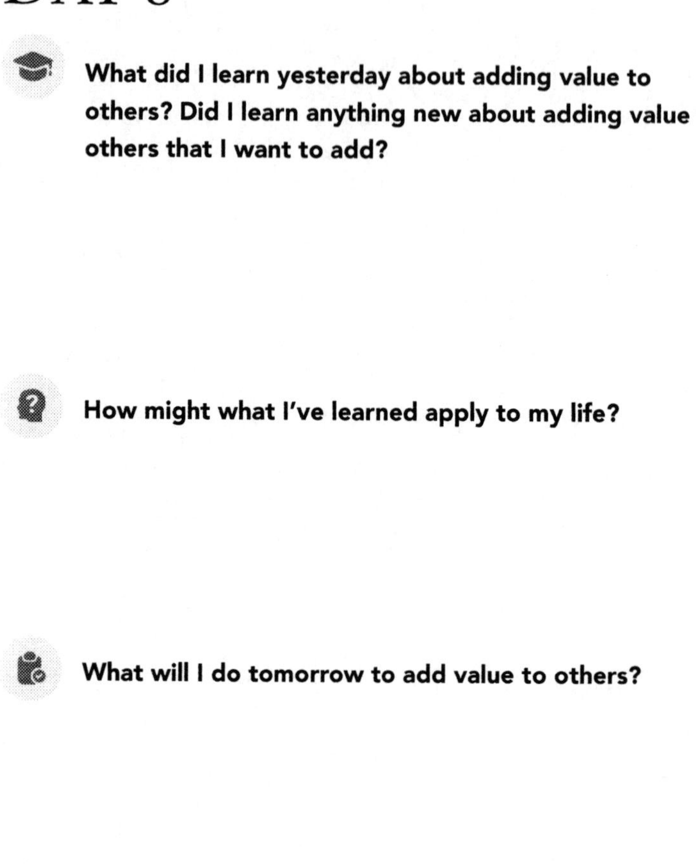

What did I learn yesterday about adding value to others? Did I learn anything new about adding value to others that I want to add?

How might what I've learned apply to my life?

What will I do tomorrow to add value to others?

Reflection:

DAY 9

What did I learn yesterday about adding value to others? Did I learn anything new about adding value to others that I want to add?

How might what I've learned apply to my life?

What will I do tomorrow to add value to others?

Reflection:

DAY 10

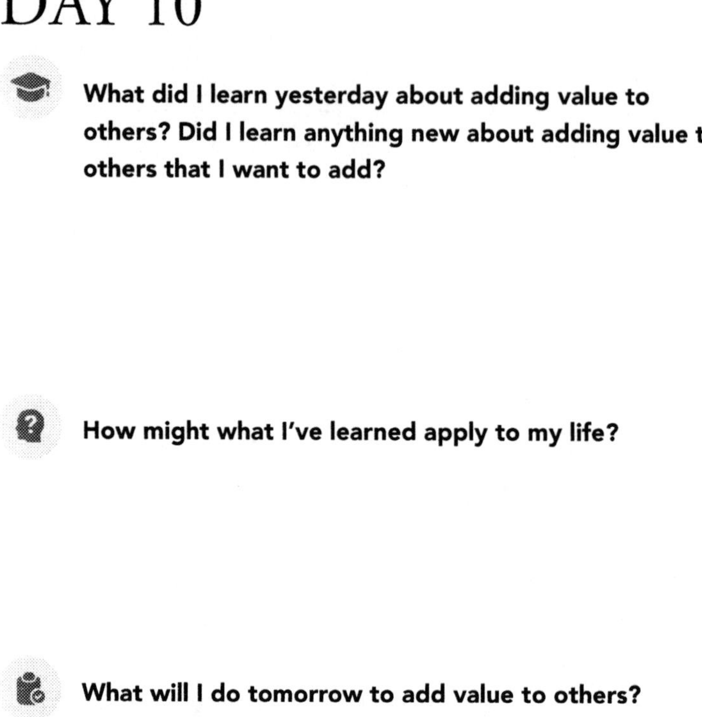

What did I learn yesterday about adding value to others? Did I learn anything new about adding value to others that I want to add?

How might what I've learned apply to my life?

What will I do tomorrow to add value to others?

Reflection:

"The things you do for yourself are gone when you are gone, but the things you do for others remain as your legacy." —Kalu Kalu

DAY 11

What did I learn yesterday about adding value to others? Did I learn anything new about adding value to others that I want to add?

How might what I've learned apply to my life?

What will I do tomorrow to add value to others?

Reflection:

"Not adding value is the same as taking it away." —*Seth Godin*

DAY 12

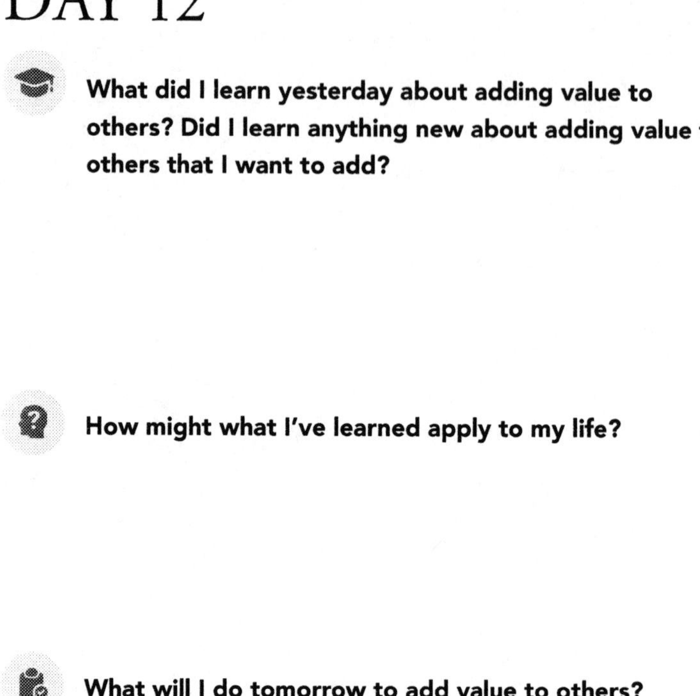

What did I learn yesterday about adding value to others? Did I learn anything new about adding value to others that I want to add?

How might what I've learned apply to my life?

What will I do tomorrow to add value to others?

Reflection:

DAY 13

What did I learn yesterday about adding value to others? Did I learn anything new about adding value to others that I want to add?

How might what I've learned apply to my life?

What will I do tomorrow to add value to others?

Reflection:

DAY 14

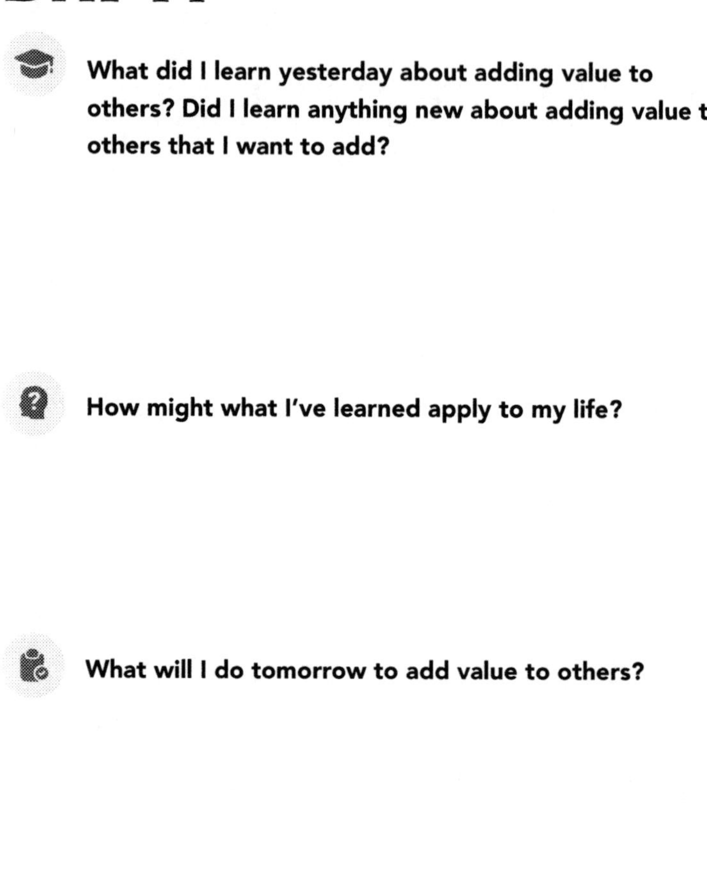

What did I learn yesterday about adding value to others? Did I learn anything new about adding value to others that I want to add?

How might what I've learned apply to my life?

What will I do tomorrow to add value to others?

Reflection:

"When you live your life in alignment with a purpose that is centered on selflessly adding value for others, opportunities become abundant and your life becomes fulfilled." —Hal Elrod

"If you're not doing something with your life, then it doesn't matter how long you live. If you're doing something with your life, then it doesn't matter how short your life may be. A life is not measured by years lived, but by its usefulness. If you are giving, loving, serving, helping, encouraging, and adding value to others, then you're living a life that counts!" —John C. Maxwell

Your Visualization Exercise—Adding Value to Others

My visualization for adding value to others is the front door of our company that I walk through every day. Each day, as I get out of my car, get my backpack and coat, and make my way to the front door, I begin to think about who I will add value to that day. My role as CEO of our company is to teach and develop leaders and to add value to their beliefs about leadership; but more importantly, it's to help them believe in themselves. When you arrive at your place of business, begin to think about who you will add value to that day.

Close your eyes and picture what adding value to others looks like to you. This will be the picture that will represent how you think about adding value to others. Make sure it is a picture of something you do every day.

Close your eyes again and visualize your picture of serving first, then building trust, then living your values, then listening to understand, then thinking about your thinking, and finally adding value to others. Spend a few minutes thinking about your journey and your pictures of the first six behaviors.

Write your true life visualization of what adding value to others looks like to you.

Chapter 8

Behavior No. 7 — DEMONSTRATE COURAGE

"Courage is what it takes to stand up and speak; courage is also what it takes to sit down and listen." —Winston Churchill

To talk about courage is to talk about accountability. Accountability is an obligation or willingness to accept responsibility and/or to account for your actions. It's very important that servant leaders have the courage to do what we say we're going to do. At the Servant Leadership Institute, we don't say "let's walk our talk," we say "let's behave our talk."

There is a difficult side of leadership, and it requires courage to get through it. That means we have the courage to face today's challenges, the courage to have the tough conversations, the courage to help others deal with the unfolding events in their lives, and the courage to live the values we believe in. And we have to have the courage to help others change their behavior on an ongoing basis to bring about their transformation. We really need to listen to understand what's going on with our people, and it takes courage to keep our mouths closed and our ears open.

There are things I'd love to do every day, and there are things I don't like to do. Given a choice, of course, I'd pick what I like to do, but that may not be the best thing for my organization. As a leader, I have to show up and say, "What is the best thing for me to do for my team today?" Have the courage to do what's needed for your organization.

Demonstrating courage as a leader could include:

- Challenging non-useful beliefs that keep people from going where they want to go
- Confronting reality about what is really going on in your organization

- Delivering results, while focusing on the process of how results are obtained rather than the results themselves
- Facing our shortcomings, being transparent, and asking for help—having the courage to really look at our heart and our behaviors and change what we're doing
- Having the difficult conversation, with the goal of restoring relationships to what they once were

As you grow and transform and face your fears, you'll find you're building courage to do the things leaders must do. Journal about the things you face for the next 14 days and the courage needed to respond.

DAY 1

What did I learn about demonstrating courage?

How might what I've learned apply to my life?

What will I do to demonstrate courage?

Reflection:

DAY 2

What did I learn yesterday about demonstrating courage? Did I learn anything new about demonstrating courage that I want to add?

How might what I've learned apply to my life?

What will I do to demonstrate courage?

Reflection:

DAY 3

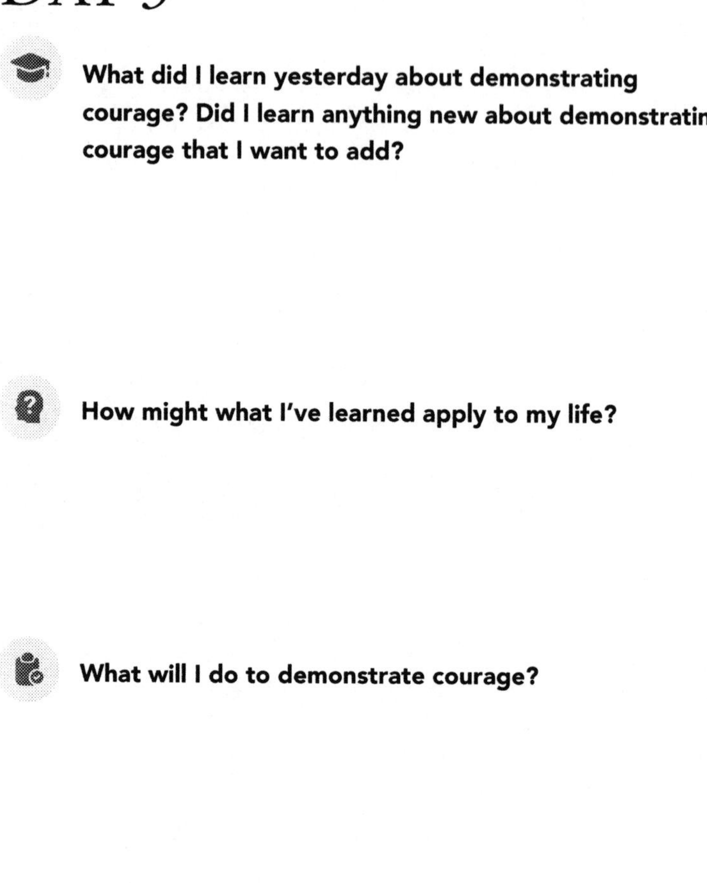

What did I learn yesterday about demonstrating courage? Did I learn anything new about demonstrating courage that I want to add?

How might what I've learned apply to my life?

What will I do to demonstrate courage?

Reflection:

"One man with courage is a majority." —Thomas Jefferson

DAY 4

What did I learn yesterday about demonstrating courage? Did I learn anything new about demonstrating courage that I want to add?

How might what I've learned apply to my life?

What will I do to demonstrate courage?

Reflection:

DAY 5

What did I learn yesterday about demonstrating courage? Did I learn anything new about demonstrating courage that I want to add?

How might what I've learned apply to my life?

What will I do to demonstrate courage?

Reflection:

DAY 6

What did I learn yesterday about demonstrating courage? Did I learn anything new about demonstrating courage that I want to add?

How might what I've learned apply to my life?

What will I do to demonstrate courage?

Reflection:

"Few men are willing to brave the disapproval of their fellows, the censure of their colleagues, the wrath of their society. Moral courage is a rarer commodity than bravery in battle or great intelligence. Yet it is the one essential, vital quality of those who seek to change a world which yields most painfully to change."
— Ernest Hemingway, A Farewell to Arms

DAY 7

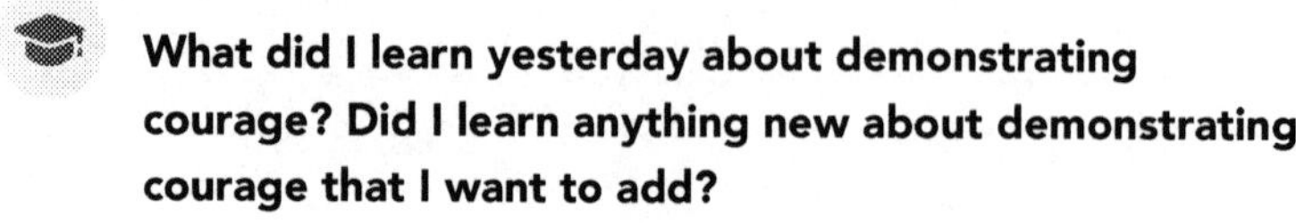

What did I learn yesterday about demonstrating courage? Did I learn anything new about demonstrating courage that I want to add?

How might what I've learned apply to my life?

What will I do to demonstrate courage?

Reflection:

DAY 8

What did I learn yesterday about demonstrating courage? Did I learn anything new about demonstrating courage that I want to add?

How might what I've learned apply to my life?

What will I do to demonstrate courage?

Reflection:

"Courage is grace under pressure." —Ernest Hemingway

DAY 9

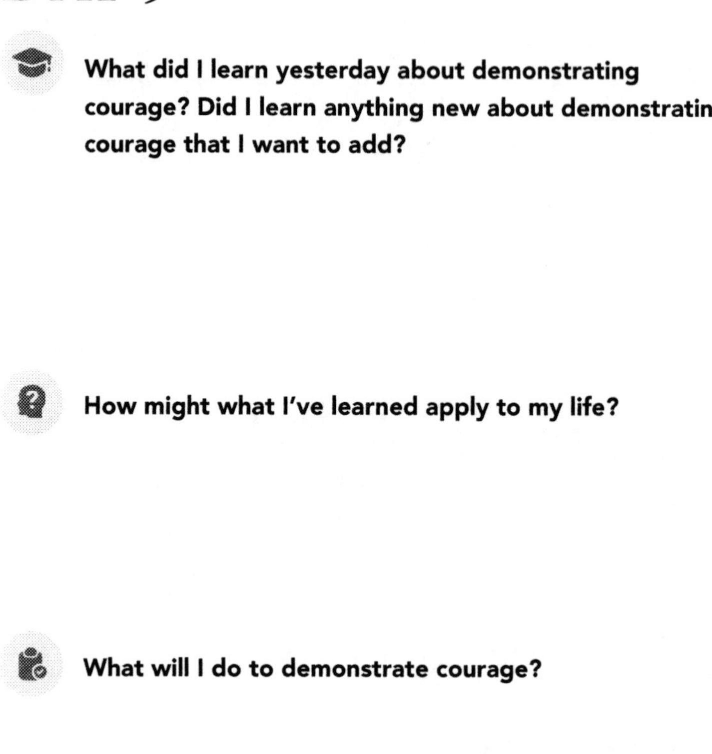

What did I learn yesterday about demonstrating courage? Did I learn anything new about demonstrating courage that I want to add?

How might what I've learned apply to my life?

What will I do to demonstrate courage?

Reflection:

DAY 10

What did I learn yesterday about demonstrating courage? Did I learn anything new about demonstrating courage that I want to add?

How might what I've learned apply to my life?

What will I do to demonstrate courage?

Reflection:

DAY 11

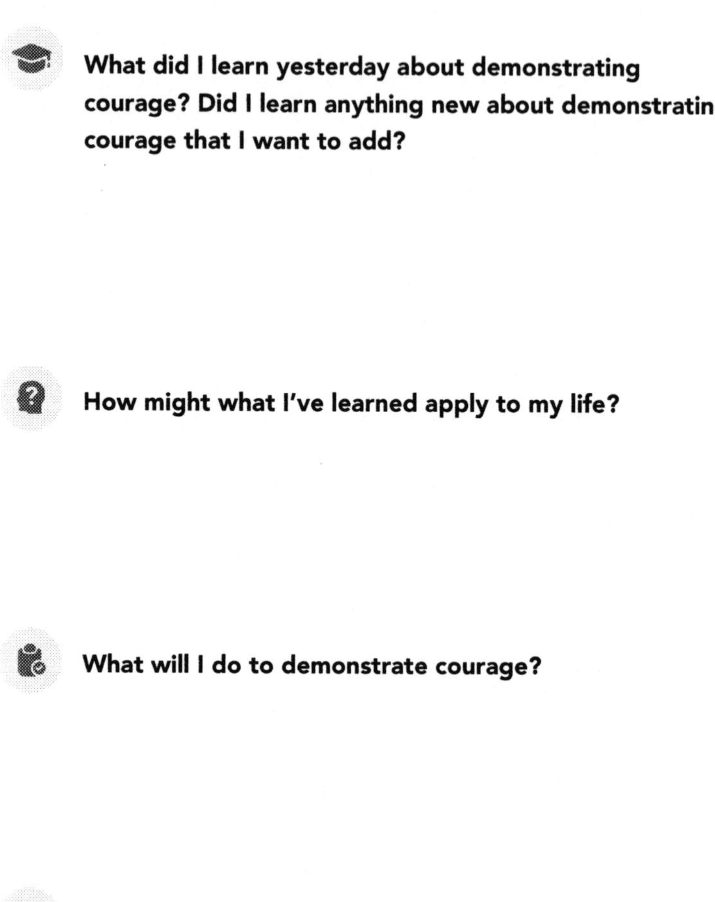

What did I learn yesterday about demonstrating courage? Did I learn anything new about demonstrating courage that I want to add?

How might what I've learned apply to my life?

What will I do to demonstrate courage?

Reflection:

"Courage is the capacity to confront what can be imagined."
—Leo Rosten

DAY 12

What did I learn yesterday about demonstrating courage? Did I learn anything new about demonstrating courage that I want to add?

How might what I've learned apply to my life?

What will I do to demonstrate courage?

Reflection:

DAY 13

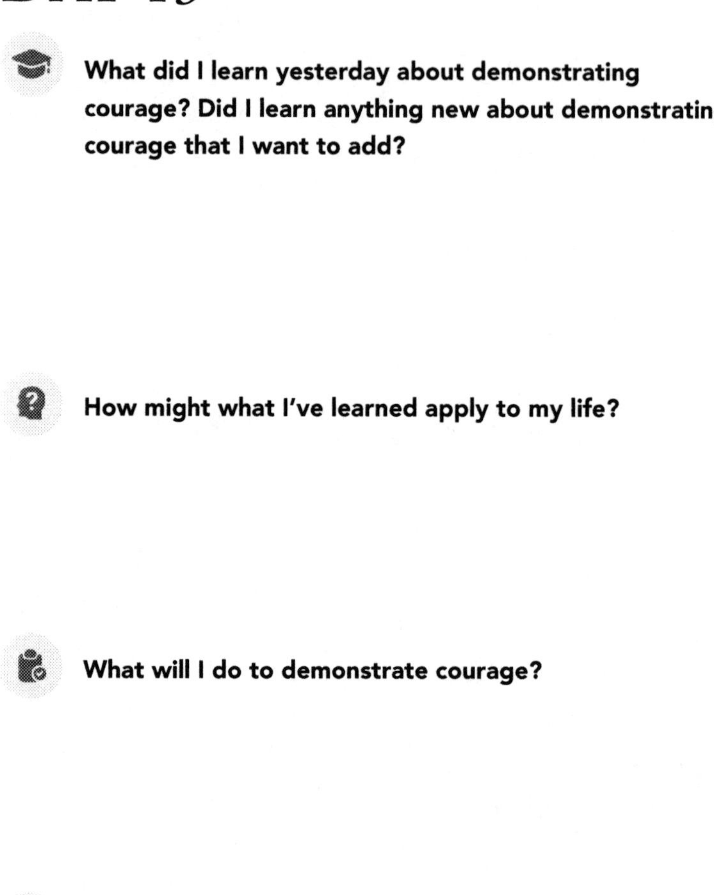

What did I learn yesterday about demonstrating courage? Did I learn anything new about demonstrating courage that I want to add?

How might what I've learned apply to my life?

What will I do to demonstrate courage?

Reflection:

"Have the courage to say no. Have the courage to face the truth. Do the right thing because it is right. These are the magic keys to living your life with integrity." —W. Clement Stone

DAY 14

What did I learn yesterday about demonstrating courage? Did I learn anything new about demonstrating courage that I want to add?

How might what I've learned apply to my life?

What will I do to demonstrate courage?

Reflection:

> *"I learned that courage was not the absence of fear, but the triumph over it. The brave man is not he who does not feel afraid, but he who conquers that fear."*
> *—Nelson Mandela*

Your Visualization Exercise — Demonstrate Courage

My visualization of demonstrating courage is, after I walk through the front door at work, going upstairs to my office and meeting with Lisa, my Executive Assistant. Usually my first response after reviewing my calendar for the day is, "No way!" Lisa tells me, "Yes, you can and you will." I am not a schedule type person, nor do I like uncomfortable conversations, so I really don't like it when Lisa reminds me we have already rescheduled the meeting twice before and she's not going to reschedule it again. She tells me I need to have that courageous conversation, usually regarding some type of behavioral issues. The real courage, though, is to approach the conversation with the right motive. Having the right motive in dealing with others requires courage. Servant leaders today need to show up, stand up, and speak up—all with the right motives—to inspire and equip those they influence.

Close your eyes and picture what demonstrating courage looks like to you. This will be the picture that will represent the way you demonstrate courage. Make sure it is a picture of something you do every day.

Close your eyes again and visualize your picture of serving first, then building trust, then living your values, then listening to understand, then thinking about your thinking, then adding value to others, and finally demonstrating courage. Spend a few minutes thinking about your journey and the pictures of the first seven behaviors.

Write your true life visualization of what demonstrating courage looks like to you.

Chapter 9

Behavior No. 8 — INCREASE YOUR INFLUENCE

"You can never really live anyone else's life, not even your child's. The influence you exert is through your own life, and what you've become yourself." —Eleanor Roosevelt

Influencing from a servant leadership perspective is inspiring and equipping others, compared to a perspective or position of power, manipulation, and serving your own agenda.

Your transformation journey through the first seven servant leadership behaviors—serving first, building trust, living your values, listening to understand, thinking about your thinking, adding value, and demonstrating courage—is a natural lead-in to increasing your influence. At that point, your influence will come from your behavior and not from your talk.

As you increase your influence as a servant leader, you're always looking to have a positive outcome in the lives of others and to engage in positive change. Once you start influencing others in that way, you'll hear about their stories and from some, receive notes of appreciation for the impact you've had on their lives. Their stories are what will keep you going.

You really do have influence on so many others in your life, and some you don't even know. I am always amazed at the influence we have over each other. We are a society of people who are concerned about what others think of us, whether we know them or not. Influence is a form of power we all have; the real question is, will you use your influence for the good of others or for yourself? Will your goal be to just influence those people for your own desires, or is your real goal to help them be successful? And when they are successful, do you give them the credit or do you take the credit for yourself? Remember, you're only as good as the people you have working for you, so if you want great results, have great relationships with the people you influence and create win-win situations with their perspectives in mind.

As you seek to influence others, there are several methods you can use:

- You can lead by example (role modeling).
- You can motivate, support, and guide (coaching).
- You can teach with hands-on instruction (mentoring).
- You can provide professional guidance and advice (counseling).

The bottom line is, you have to care and invest your time. Motive and influence both reflect your heart, and together they can be powerful. Servant leaders chose to serve first, so we have already decided to use our influence to help others. As you think about your influence, don't fall into the trap of thinking you don't influence anyone. I challenge you to look for signs of your influence over the next 14 days. You will be surprised. Journal on...

DAY 1

What did I learn about increasing my influence?

How might what I've learned apply to my life?

What will I do tomorrow to increase my influence?

Reflection:

DAY 2

What did I learn yesterday about increasing my influence? Did I learn anything new about increasing my influence that I want to add?

How might what I've learned apply to my life?

What will I do tomorrow to increase my influence?

Reflection:

"The purpose of influence is to 'speak up for those who have no influence' (Pr.31:8). It's not about you." —Rick Warren

DAY 3

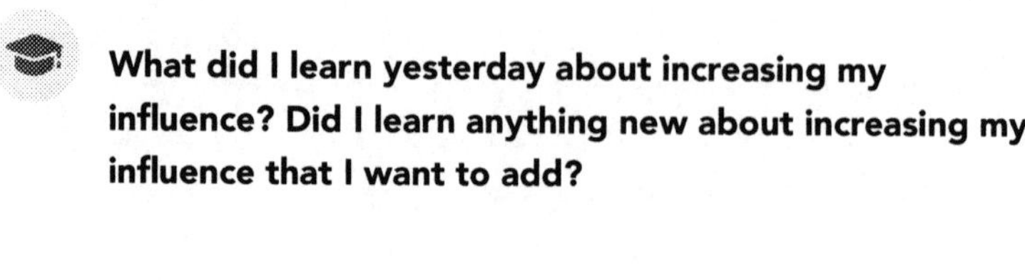

What did I learn yesterday about increasing my influence? Did I learn anything new about increasing my influence that I want to add?

How might what I've learned apply to my life?

What will I do tomorrow to increase my influence?

Reflection:

DAY 4

What did I learn yesterday about increasing my influence? Did I learn anything new about increasing my influence that I want to add?

How might what I've learned apply to my life?

What will I do tomorrow to increase my influence?

Reflection:

"A life isn't significant except for its impact on other lives."
—Jackie Robinson

DAY 5

What did I learn yesterday about increasing my influence? Did I learn anything new about increasing my influence that I want to add?

How might what I've learned apply to my life?

What will I do tomorrow to increase my influence?

Reflection:

DAY 6

What did I learn yesterday about increasing my influence? Did I learn anything new about increasing my influence that I want to add?

How might what I've learned apply to my life?

What will I do tomorrow to increase my influence?

Reflection:

"Leadership is not about a title or a designation. It's about impact, influence and inspiration. Impact involves getting results, influence is about spreading the passion you have for your work, and you have to inspire teammates and customers." —Robin S. Sharma

DAY 7

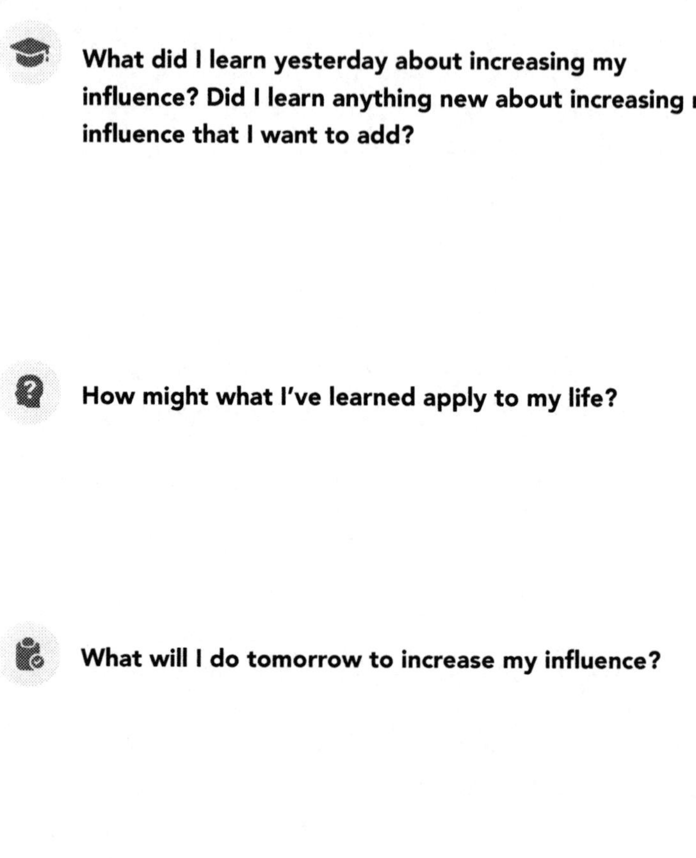

What did I learn yesterday about increasing my influence? Did I learn anything new about increasing my influence that I want to add?

How might what I've learned apply to my life?

What will I do tomorrow to increase my influence?

Reflection:

DAY 8

What did I learn yesterday about increasing my influence? Did I learn anything new about increasing my influence that I want to add?

How might what I've learned apply to my life?

What will I do tomorrow to increase my influence?

Reflection:

DAY 9

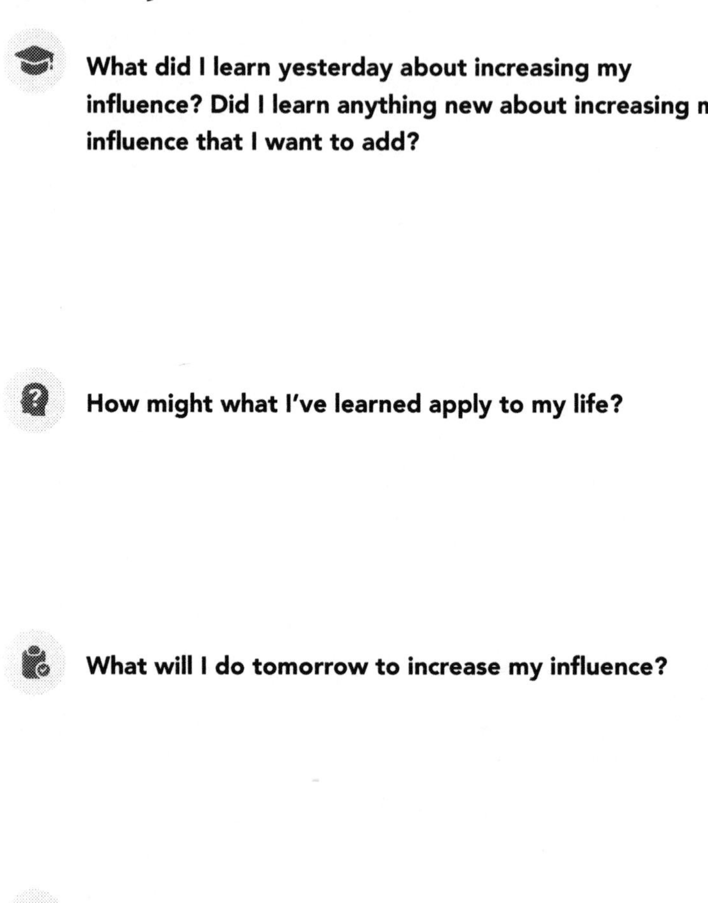

What did I learn yesterday about increasing my influence? Did I learn anything new about increasing my influence that I want to add?

How might what I've learned apply to my life?

What will I do tomorrow to increase my influence?

Reflection:

"Blessed is the influence of one true, loving human soul on another."
—George Eliot

DAY 10

What did I learn yesterday about increasing my influence? Did I learn anything new about increasing my influence that I want to add?

How might what I've learned apply to my life?

What will I do tomorrow to increase my influence?

Reflection:

DAY 11

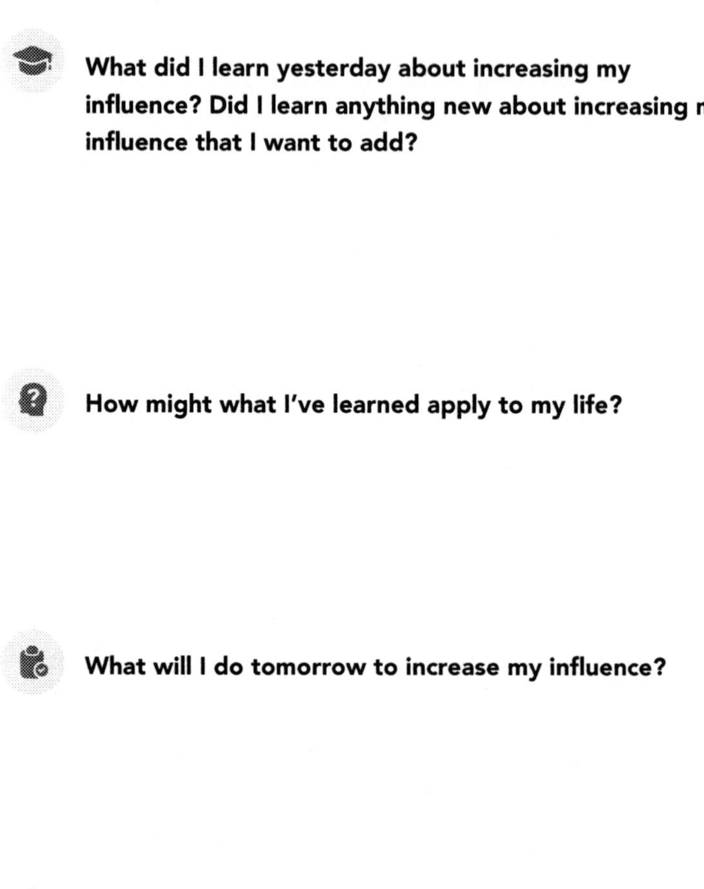

What did I learn yesterday about increasing my influence? Did I learn anything new about increasing my influence that I want to add?

How might what I've learned apply to my life?

What will I do tomorrow to increase my influence?

Reflection:

"Example is not the main thing in influencing others. It is the only thing." —Albert Schweitzer

DAY 12

What did I learn yesterday about increasing my influence? Did I learn anything new about increasing my influence that I want to add?

How might what I've learned apply to my life?

What will I do tomorrow to increase my influence?

Reflection:

DAY 13

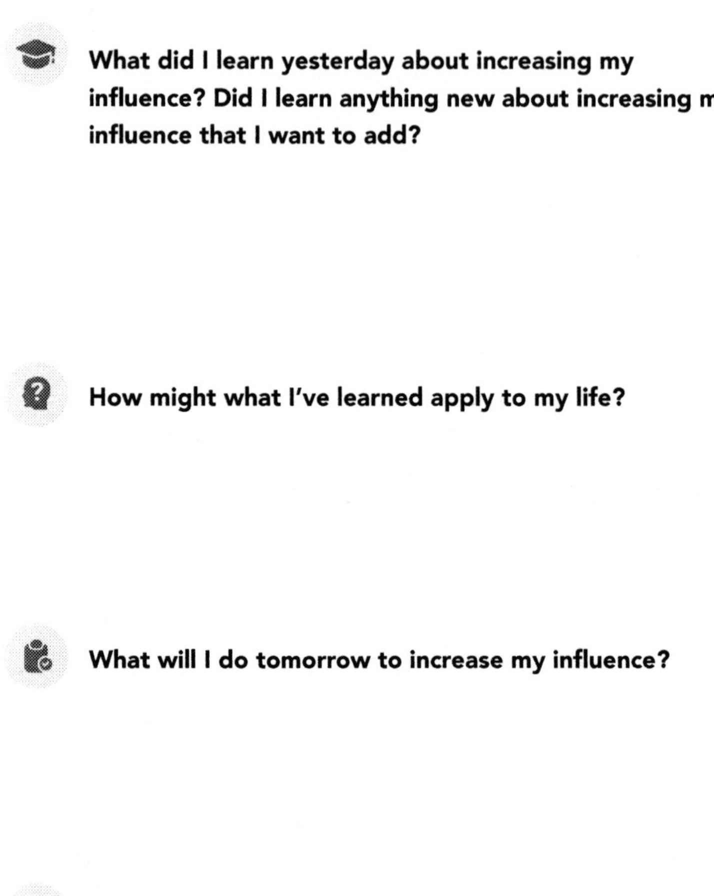

What did I learn yesterday about increasing my influence? Did I learn anything new about increasing my influence that I want to add?

How might what I've learned apply to my life?

What will I do tomorrow to increase my influence?

Reflection:

"The key to successful leadership today is influence, not authority."
—Ken Blanchard

DAY 14

What did I learn yesterday about increasing my influence? Did I learn anything new about increasing my influence that I want to add?

How might what I've learned apply to my life?

What will I do tomorrow to increase my influence?

Reflection:

"Leadership is not about titles, positions or flowcharts. It is about one life influencing another." —John C. Maxwell

"We never know which lives we influence, or when, or why."
—Stephen King, 11/22/63

Your Visualization Exercise — Increase Your Influence

When I visualize increasing my influence, I think about an individual on our leadership team who I need to spend more time with to develop that person's leadership skills or someone who has asked for some time for mentoring or coaching. Our influence can be indirect: people watch what we say and do, and even what we don't say or do. Really, all of us are leaders and we all have influence over others. If you're a parent, you know when your young children do or say something you don't like, they have often learned that behavior from their parents! Right? We really don't know which lives we will influence, when it will happen or why it happens. Be aware you are always influencing someone.

Close your eyes and picture what increasing your influence looks like to you. This will be the picture that will represent increasing your influence. Make sure it's a picture of something you do every day.

Close your eyes again and visualize your picture of serving first, then building trust, then living your values, then listening to understand, then thinking about your thinking, then adding value to others, then demonstrating courage, and now increasing your influence. Spend a few minutes thinking about your journey and the pictures of the first eight behaviors.

Write your true life visualization of what increasing your influence looks like to you.

Chapter 10

Behavior No. 9 —
LIVE YOUR TRANSFORMATION

> *"Transformation is a process, and as life happens there are tons of ups and downs. It's a journey of discovery—there are moments on mountaintops and moments in deep valleys of despair."*
> —*Rick Warren*

Transformation is a change in form, appearance, nature, or character. The self-help industry in America (books, audio-books, videos, seminars and coaches) is over a billion-dollar industry, which tells us we all have a great desire to change who we are. Most of us have a desire to serve others, but that desire has been buried deep within us because of life's pressures; part of our transformation involves helping that desire to serve come out.

You have already made the decision to be a better leader. You've invested in yourself. You've read books, you've likely talked to mentors and coaches, you've learned from others as well as your own experiences and through the behaviors of servant leadership, and now it's time to let that investment out, day to day, with everyone you come into contact with.

A word of caution, it isn't that difficult to live your transformation with those you like as individuals, or others who share the same values and who desire to live their lives for the sake of others. It is a real challenge, however, to live your transformation with those you may not get along with or who may not share your values or your desire to help and serve others.

When I teach others about living their transformation, I share the story of walking down a hallway at work and seeing someone at the other end walking toward me. That person is one I know who, given the chance, will stop and tell me everything that is wrong with the company and its leaders, and why the current project or program has no chance of being successful. You know—those who have nothing positive to say. When I see that individual walking toward me, I want to take a detour into a side office so I can avoid the conversation. That's not quite living my transformation, is it? If I am serious about being a servant leader and living my transformation, I will stop and say "Hi," ask how they are doing, and either talk to them for a few minutes if I can, or say "I would love to talk to you, but I can't until a later time."

Living your transformation takes discipline and courage to stay the course. You're not going to be perfect; you will make mistakes. Transformation takes time, but if you strive for excellence and not perfection, I know you can do it. Your life will definitely be better because of it. Enjoy the next several weeks learning how you can live your transformation.

DAY 1

What did I learn about living my transformation?

How might what I've learned apply to my life?

What will I do tomorrow to live my transformation?

Reflection:

DAY 2

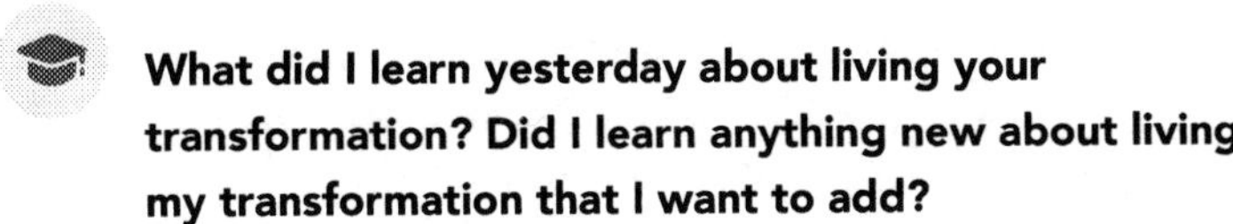

What did I learn yesterday about living your transformation? Did I learn anything new about living my transformation that I want to add?

How might what I've learned apply to my life?

What will I do tomorrow to live my transformation?

Reflection:

DAY 3

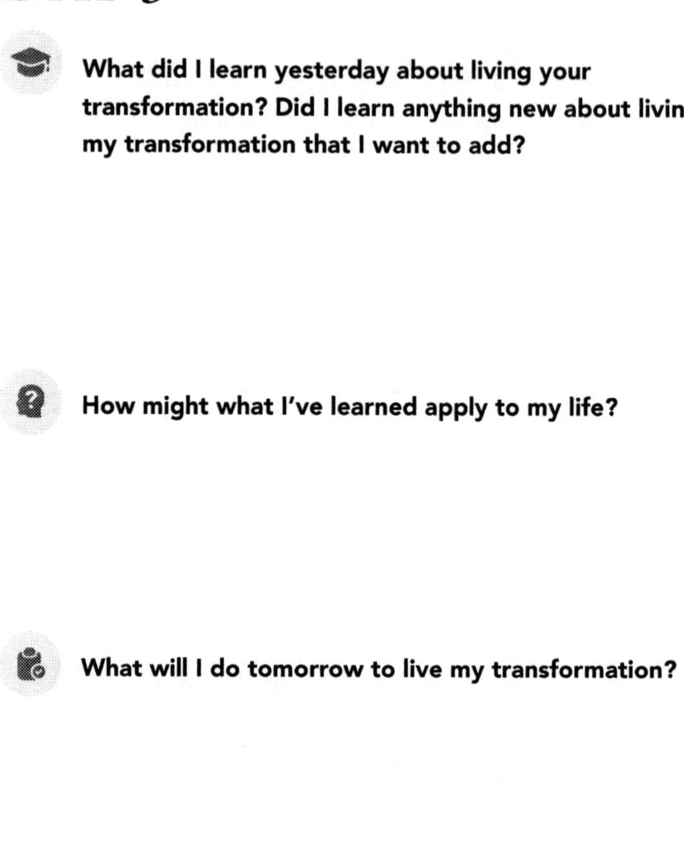

What did I learn yesterday about living your transformation? Did I learn anything new about living my transformation that I want to add?

How might what I've learned apply to my life?

What will I do tomorrow to live my transformation?

Reflection:

DAY 4

What did I learn yesterday about living your transformation? Did I learn anything new about living my transformation that I want to add?

How might what I've learned apply to my life?

What will I do tomorrow to live my transformation?

Reflection:

DAY 5

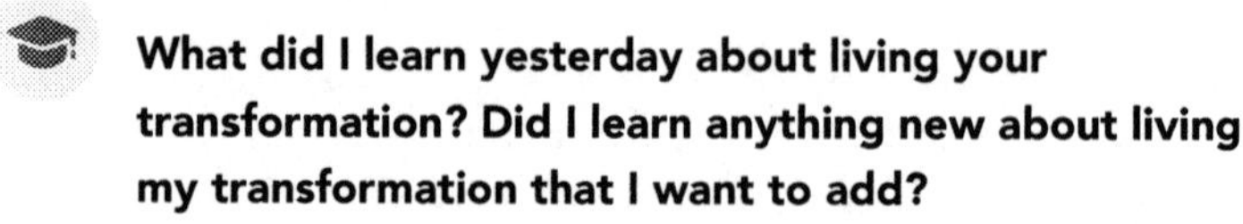

What did I learn yesterday about living your transformation? Did I learn anything new about living my transformation that I want to add?

How might what I've learned apply to my life?

What will I do tomorrow to live my transformation?

Reflection:

DAY 6

What did I learn yesterday about living your transformation? Did I learn anything new about living my transformation that I want to add?

How might what I've learned apply to my life?

What will I do tomorrow to live my transformation?

Reflection:

"Life is a moving, breathing thing. We have to be willing to constantly evolve. Perfection is constant transformation." —*Nia Peeples*

DAY 7

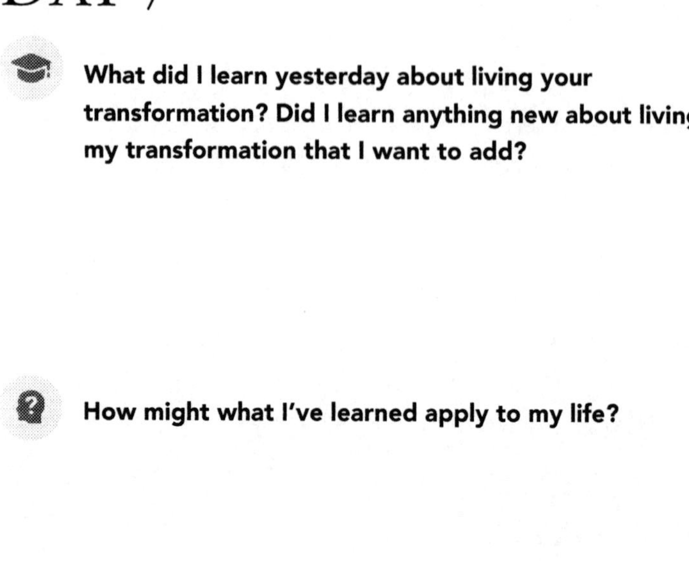

What did I learn yesterday about living your transformation? Did I learn anything new about living my transformation that I want to add?

How might what I've learned apply to my life?

What will I do tomorrow to live my transformation?

Reflection:

DAY 8

What did I learn yesterday about living your transformation? Did I learn anything new about living my transformation that I want to add?

How might what I've learned apply to my life?

What will I do tomorrow to live my transformation?

Reflection:

DAY 9

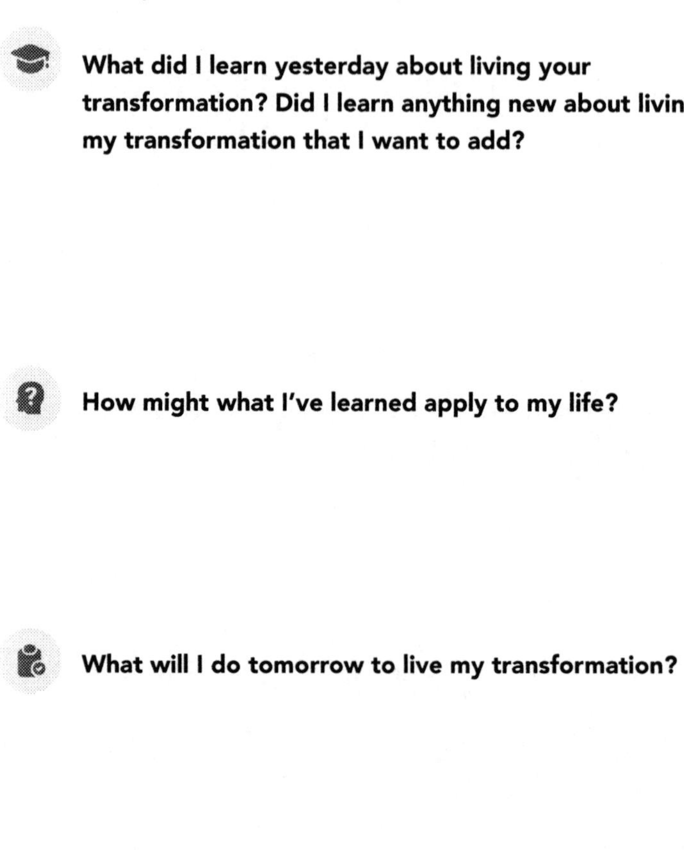

What did I learn yesterday about living your transformation? Did I learn anything new about living my transformation that I want to add?

How might what I've learned apply to my life?

What will I do tomorrow to live my transformation?

Reflection:

DAY 10

What did I learn yesterday about living your transformation? Did I learn anything new about living my transformation that I want to add?

How might what I've learned apply to my life?

What will I do tomorrow to live my transformation?

Reflection:

DAY 11

What did I learn yesterday about living your transformation? Did I learn anything new about living my transformation that I want to add?

How might what I've learned apply to my life?

What will I do tomorrow to live my transformation?

Reflection:

"Don't let what you can't do interfere with what you can do."
—John Wooden

DAY 12

What did I learn yesterday about living your transformation? Did I learn anything new about living my transformation that I want to add?

How might what I've learned apply to my life?

What will I do tomorrow to live my transformation?

Reflection:

DAY 13

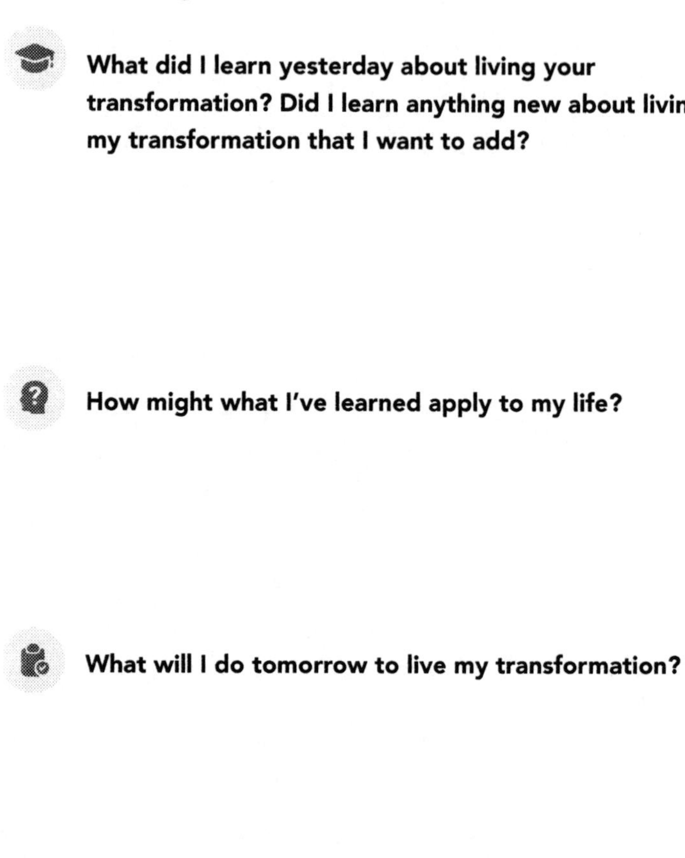

What did I learn yesterday about living your transformation? Did I learn anything new about living my transformation that I want to add?

How might what I've learned apply to my life?

What will I do tomorrow to live my transformation?

Reflection:

DAY 14

What did I learn yesterday about living your transformation? Did I learn anything new about living my transformation that I want to add?

How might what I've learned apply to my life?

What will I do tomorrow to live my transformation?

Reflection:

As human beings, our greatness lies not so much in being able to remake the world—that is the myth of the atomic age—as in being able to remake ourselves.
— Mahatma Gandhi

Your Visualization Exercise — Living Your Transformation

When I visualize living my transformation, I think about an individual on our leadership team who I'm not in sync with. We may not agree on how the purpose of the company should be executed, or our personalities may conflict (we may be too much alike). There are no excuses for leaders to take a break from behaving in an appropriate way, in accordance with our values. So I think about this person and what I need to do as his or her leader to improve the relationship. It's my responsibility to ensure my behavior aligns with my talk.

Close your eyes and picture what living your transformation looks like to you. This will be the picture that will represent living your transformation. Make sure it is a picture of something you do every day.

Close your eyes again and visualize your picture of serving first, then building trust, then living your values, then listening to understand, then thinking about your thinking, then adding value to others, then demonstrating courage, then increasing your influence, and finally living your transformation. Spend a few minutes thinking about your journey and your pictures of all nine behaviors.

Write your true life visualization of what living your transformation looks like to you.

Chapter 11

THE PERSON IN THE MIRROR IS WATCHING

Congratulations! You have made it through 18 weeks of learning, understanding, application and reflection on the nine behaviors of servant leadership. I want to leave you with a poem I discovered after both my parents had passed away, when I was going through the last of their files. It was typed on an old typewriter, and the paper was faded and worn. No author was shown on the poem, which made me wonder if my great grandfather, who was a writer, wrote it. I set it aside and then shared it with the staff at the Servant Leadership Institute. After reading the poem with some emotion, we started to do some research. We discovered that it was written in 1934 by Peter Dale Wimbrow, Sr. I want to thank the family of Dale Wimbrow for allowing us to use the poem in our teaching and publish it in this journal. (Note: I've included the poem as I found it in my parents' belongings. This version includes a few very small differences from the original poem.)

The Man in the Glass

By Peter Dale Wimbrow, Sr.

When you get what you want in your struggle for self
And the world makes you king for a day
Just go to the mirror and look at yourself
And see what that man has to say.

For it isn't your father, or mother, or wife
Whose judgment upon you must pass
The fellow whose verdict counts most in your life
Is the one staring back from the glass.

He's the fellow to please — never mind all the rest
For he's with you, clear to the end
And you've passed your most difficult, dangerous test
If the man in the glass is your friend.

You may fool the whole world down the pathway of years
And get pats on the back as you pass
But your final reward will be heartache and tears
If you've cheated the man in the glass.

ꟷ

Living your life for the sake of others using the nine behaviors of servant leadership will change your life and the lives of those around you. As I reflect on my own career, I wish someone would have helped me understand the value in serving others above myself while I was still in college. Changing my approach to leadership in 2003 was 30 years too late. I hope you have been influenced by our work at the institute. We are here to serve you and would love to hear from you. Please feel free to contact us. We would enjoy hearing your story about your journey.

We are on this journey with you. Now, one last time, close your eyes and go through your visualization for the nine behaviors.

One Last Visualization Exercise

Close your eyes and picture a family member, friend or someone at work who you desire to have a better relationship with. Think about serving that person, building trust, listening to understand them. Visualize their reaction when they realize you really care for them, want to help them, love them, have a true desire for a better relationship. Do you see a smile, or maybe some tears of joy? Embrace the reaction you see in your mind and live it every day.

Live your life to the fullest, caring for and serving others through servant leadership. Behave your talk.™ Those around you will be forever grateful.

ADDITIONAL JOURNAL SPACE

ADDITIONAL JOURNAL SPACE

ADDITIONAL JOURNAL SPACE

ADDITIONAL JOURNAL SPACE

ADDITIONAL JOURNAL SPACE

ADDITIONAL JOURNAL SPACE

Appendix A

ART'S VISUALIZATION OF THE NINE BEHAVIORS

Serve First—Making Lori a pot of coffee when I get up in the morning

Build Trust—Driving by the school bus stop

Live Your Values—Getting on the freeway

Listen to Understand—Talking on my cell phone in the car

Think About My Thinking—Enjoying quiet time while driving to work

Add Value to Others—Entering the front door to the Datron office

Be Courageous—Discussing my schedule with Lisa, facing the daily challenge

Increase My Influence—Meeting with someone who has asked for my time

Live My Transformation—Serving everyone the same way

This is a routine I go through each day. It is real to me and easy to remember. Thank you to Fia Fasbinder, CEO of the Moxie Institute, who taught me this process. Fia is a great servant leader.

Appendix B

RECOMMENDED READING FOR SERVANT LEADERS

Publications from Servant Leadership Institute

Farmer Able, Art Barter

Our Character at Work, Todd D. Hunter

The Art of Servant Leadership: Designing Your Organization for the Sake of Others, Tony Baron

Servant Leadership Implementation Guides—Servant Leadership Institute

Culture Transformation

The Little Foxes

360 Degree Leader

Results-Driven Servant Leadership

Servant Leadership 101

The Power of a Story

The Power of Diversity

Articles from Servant Leadership Institute

When Leaders Try, Art Barter

7 Ways Servant Leadership Can Transform Your Career, Art Barter

Behave Your Way to Servant Leadership, Art Barter

Publications Recommended by Servant Leadership Institute

Dare to Serve, Cheryl Bachelder

The Speed of Trust: The One Thing that Changes Everything, Stephen M. R. Covey

Multipliers, Liz Wiseman

Intentional Living, John C. Maxwell

The Heart of a Leader: Insights on the Art of Influence, Ken Blanchard

Trust Works! Ken Blanchard, Martha Lawrence and Cynthia Olmstead

Good to Great, Jim Collins

The Leadership Challenge, James M. Kouzes and Barry S. Posner

360 Degree Leader, John C. Maxwell

The 21 Irrefutable Laws of Leadership, John C. Maxwell

Helping People Win at Work, Ken Blanchard and Garry Ridge

The Case for Servant Leadership, Keith M. Kent

Good Leaders Ask Great Questions, John C. Maxwell

Seven Pillars of Servant Leadership, James W. Sipe and Don M. Frick

The Servant as Leader, Robert K. Greenleaf

Visit the Servant Leadership Institute website at
www.servantleadershipinstitute.com

Learn more about servant leadership from Art Barter by listening to our complimentary Webinars located on our website.

Our Podcasts can be found on iTunes by searching for "Servant Leadership Institute."